EVER YOUR AFFECTIONATE

FLORRIE

EVER YOUR AFFECTIONATE

FLORRIE

LETTERS FROM
A CAVALIER KING CHARLES SPANIEL
TO HER TWO MISTRESSES

Susan Paine

With illustrations by

Gill Evans

TURRET BOOKS

First published in Great Britain 1993
by Turret Books
P.O. Box 18, Watlington
Oxfordshire OX9 5ED

Printed in Great Britain by
The Alden Press, Oxford

British Library Cataloguing in Publication Data
A catalogue record for this book is
available from the British Library

ISBN 0 9521146 0 7

To Lucy and Will

who provided the inspiration

Spaniell Gentle or the Comforter: it is also called a chamber companion, a pleasant playfellow, a pretty worme ...

Dr. Johannes Caius (1570)

Although the Toy Spaniels are unquestionably true aristocrats by nature, birth and breeding, and are most at home in a drawing-room or on a well kept lawn, they are by no means deficient in sporting proclivities, and in spite of their short noses, their scent is very keen. They thoroughly enjoy a good scamper, and are all the better for not being too much pampered. They are very good house-dogs, intelligent and affectionate, and have sympathetic coaxing little ways.

The New Book of the Dog (1907)

Let me introduce myself. I am Stoodvale Florentine, a Cavalier King Charles Spaniel, a well marked Blenheim of smaller than average stature perhaps - but then the breed has recently shown an undesirable tendency to gain in size. My resemblance to the well known painting 'A Brown and White King Charles Spaniel in a wooded landscape' by George Stubbs (1776) has often been noted, and though the jaw of the dogs of those days was perhaps a little longer, the likeness *is* remarkable.

We are of course of Royal lineage, tracing our ancestry back over three hundred years, and as such are superior dogs who know our place at the top of the canine hierarchy. A Cavalier has many unique attributes and abilities; we were bred to bring comfort both in the field and the home - we ensure that birds remain in their proper sphere - that is, in the air, and we also ensure that our owners and keepers take sufficient repose to provide us with a lap on which to settle ourselves when our sporting duty is done for the day.

I have led an interesting and varied life; I have, as it were, two mistresses - Young Mistress and Old Mistress, and as I have spent periods of time with one or the other, it has been necessary for me to correspond with the absentee owner in order to keep them informed as to my well being and activities. What follows is a compilation of these letters.

But first, I should explain the background to my two homes and provide a short summary of my early days.

9

I was born in Devon, and naturally have many distinguished forbears, a great deal of red ink denoting champions appears in my pedigree. I do not remember Young Mistress choosing me - I was I believe only three weeks old at the time - but not surprisingly I was unhesitatingly selected from among my brothers and sisters for the charm and enterprise I displayed even at that tender age. I left my dear mother when little more than eight weeks old, so have few clear memories of what went before. I do recollect my nearest sister, a rather weakly little thing, with very unfortunately a *white ear*. However I heard later that even with this infirmity, she found an excellent home with the local vicar - at a reduced price of course, and did very well. I remember more exactly a long journey by car, when, although placed initially in a cardboard box, I soon escaped from this cheerless container and made myself much more comfortable on Young Mistress's lap.

... I was glad of her company and warmth in the basket

Our destination was a pleasant country house, and a number of admiring humans, large and smaller, made much of me on my arrival. An elderly long low dog, which I later learnt was one of the Dachshund breed, was friendly. Even to one with my confidence and poise new surroundings can be a little intimidating, and I was glad of her company and her warmth in the basket. I was less glad when I found I was expected to spend the night alone, and in a box - even though it was placed beside the Aga. I made strong complaint, but the Man of the household appeared and spoke severely. With the superior intelligence of my breed, I realised that it was prudent to comply, and that graceful acceptance of this regime would soon demonstrate my capability to remain continent at night and my fitness to be left unconfined.

The days passed and I became familiar with the house and grounds, which I found on the whole appropriate for my needs. A proper amount of attention was paid to me, meals came regularly and were of good quality and I could stroll outside at my pleasure during the day. Come evening time, I was offered a choice of laps - and once I had decided which person I would favour, I would settle down

I became familiar with the house and grounds ...

at once and so was always sought after. It has become clear to me over the years that, whilst a Cavalier is born to be a lap dog, others are not. The fidgetings, scrabbling about and general angularity of, for example, the terrier breeds when they attempt to emulate Us and lay claim to a lap is painful to observe and disagreeable to their owners. Understandably the aspiring dog is usually returned to the ground. We of course were Royal comforters three hundred years ago. Instinctive to us the light spring up, the immediate settling down, subtly moulding ourselves to a position satisfactory to us and to our humans. The secret of remaining undisturbed is to maintain complete stillness; a light snore can even be employed to emphasise your need for peace and quiet. This should make certain that your human will also remain still and seated, requesting others to fetch the coffee/newspaper/change the CD and so forth, because 'it would be a shame to move Florrie'. A Cavalier is born with this skill.

But I digress and anticipate. Experience, sharp observation and an inborn sensitivity have brought me much knowledge, and have given me the ability to cope in a dignified manner with some difficult and challenging situations - as will be revealed by the content of my correspondence. My early efforts perhaps demonstrate a little naivety, a touch of simplicity - but even the wisest of us have to pass through puppyhood before attaining the poise and sophistication that comes naturally to a Cavalier.

Holiday time for my Young Mistress came to an end soon after my arrival, and it was necessary for her to return to London - a place about which I then had no knowledge or understanding. With a little help from Old Mistress my letters began.

Chalk Hill
Summer, my first year

Dear Young Mistress,

I rather wish Old Mistress did not think it good for me to have green vegetable added to my otherwise very good mince and biscuit. She chops it up so small that I cannot avoid it, also old Nicky the Dachshund hovers at my elbow waiting for anything I leave and I don't want her at my dish.

... I played tug of war with the net

Sometimes I go with OM to what she calls her kitchen garden where there are rows and rows of vegetables so I suppose green breakfasts will go on. Today we got away from the spinach and went into the fruit cage - a sort of netted run. OM did not like it when I played tug of war with the net, so while she was busy picking something into a bowl, I searched for tasty bits and pieces among the straw that lay around the bushes. Suddenly I saw a movement, and smelt something that had to be followed. I crept quietly under the bush - and there was a bird *on* the ground, where I *knew* it should not be. I made a run, the bird tried to fly but got stuck in the corner of the cage where it squawked and fluttered in a most exciting way. I felt brave and came up closer and barked to encourage it to get airbound. OM joined me and picked up the bird, while I barked

13

even more. We took it to the cage door and once outside it flew properly away. We went to look for where the bird had come in, and found a hole near where I had been playing. We tied it up with string. OM was very pleased with me for showing her the bird, but I was disappointed to be left in the kitchen next day when she went off with a bowl.

Love and kisses from Florrie.

Chalk Hill
Summer

Dear Young Mistress,

I enjoyed our walks in the fields last weekend, though I don't understand why you and OM stopped me chewing on those delicious little heaps left by the otherwise dull creatures called sheep, or why you didn't approve of me rolling in the black feathers I found under the hedge and so covering myself with a truly beautiful smell. It was a nasty shock to be put into the washing up bowl and to have really foul stuff called disinfectant tipped all over me. But wrapping myself up in the sofa cushions afterwards made a much better job of getting my coat dry than that old towel.

... to be put into the washing up bowl ...

This week I've discovered very interesting whiffs of this and that are to be found down the lane just outside the big white gate. Other dogs sometimes pass by and leave intriguing messages. Unfortunately OM does not like me making these short excursions, although I always come back after she's shouted for a few minutes. A gate covered with wire mesh has appeared across the back yard entrance, limiting me to the yard and lower garden. I was insulted to hear OM saying I was the colour of gravel and might not be seen by car drivers - I can assure you that my brown patches are darkening rapidly, and the one down my right hind leg is becoming a fine rich chestnut.

I have met a horse or two. They are very tall; OM has warned me to keep well clear of their feet, which are nearly as large as me and edged with metal. I may be young but I have quite enough sense of self preservation to see this is sensible advice.

I believe next week we are going to visit a place called Exmoor.

Ever your loving Florrie.

On Exmoor
August

Dear Young Mistress,

We have arrived safely - after a great to-do of packing up. Many boxes and parcels were piled up in the hall; I had a good sniff through them and was just making progress at the corner of a large cardboard box - covered in pictures of apples, but by the messages coming from my nose full of far more appealing things like biscuit and butter. I find cardboard a very satisfying substance on which to exercise my teeth, all the more so if there's a promise of delights beyond, but I was disturbed by OM, who picked me up, quite roughly, and shut me and Nicky in the *stable*. I felt deeply insulted, but we consoled ourselves by having a good hunt for mice under the straw. Eventually we were let out and it was a relief to find OM a bit calmer.

.. and shut me ... in the stable

We were placed on the front seat of the horse lorry. It was the first time I'd travelled in this and it was good fun. I could see all round - the passing fields, trees and houses; sometimes other dogs at which I had a good bark. While we were going slowly through towns, several humans looked up at me admiringly and when we stopped for petrol - a horrid smell - the pump man gave me a piece of chocolate. OM seemed to feel I should have gobbled it up quickly, but I enjoyed licking it over slowly, and finally I licked up the seat too, so I can't think why she fussed so.

The journey went on a long time, but eventually we went down a thin rough lane, so steep that I nearly slid forwards onto the floor of the cab, and OM stopped the lorry. Old Nicky and I were put out and shut in a garden, new to me, but Nicky seemed to know where she was and we checked it out together. I heard the horses rattle out and the sacks of their food being heaved down. What a lot they eat - I must admit I have found some of it quite tasty, and I've learnt to look for the cubes and corn the careless animals let fall over their stable doors. The boxes of our food came next, so I soon got my supper and settled down for a snooze by the nice warm stove in the kitchen. I was pleased to find my favourite beanbag had come too.

Love from your much travelled Florrie.

16

On Exmoor

Dear Young Mistress,

This is a fine place, with many interesting smells and tasty pickings around the buildings, which have lots of dark corners to be looked into. They have a comfortable old and musty atmosphere - a hint of small animals, birds - and plenty of edible evidence that sheep and cattle have lived in them.

They have a comfortable old and musty atmosphere ...

There are less good things - this morning I encountered the river, a nasty deceptive wet thing. I was bounding along the field, saw these shiny stones before me where some interesting looking insects with glittery wings were flying about, and went to investigate. It gave me a great shock to find myself up to the elbows in horrible cold water, and I went back to the grass as quickly as I could. OM just laughed and actually tried to persuade me to pass right through what I now realised was a wide band of water. She stood in the middle and called, but I sat down firmly and barked, making it clear that a Cavalier is not a water dog and demanding that I should be carried over. This was done, though OM muttered something about 'chicken hearted', 'feeble' and 'very shallow' which I preferred not to understand. I shan't go near there again.

There are games to be had in the kitchen at night. When we have had our last run and our biscuits, the household goes quiet, out from under the cupboards come small black glossy insects - I believe they are called beetles and they are not at all difficult to catch. They make quite a good snack, their shells having a nice crunchiness. My success with these beetles has led me to look carefully around the house for other small game. OM seemed a bit shocked when I found a spider and ate it yesterday. It was a little bitter. She said you would be pleased with such activities because you particularly dislike these leggy things and that she was tired to having to get them out of the bath for you. I don't mind catching one in the bath, as long as there's *no water* in it.

Ever your loving Florrie.

Still on Exmoor

Dear Young Mistress,

I don't know why you had to spend so much time with that boring horse when you joined us here. Still we had some enjoyable walks, and I expect I shall get over the moor better when my legs have grown a little longer, though I am prepared to be carried - especially through all those wet places.

A lot of coming and going over the last few days; I understand there are to be Horse Trials on the farm. I went up the hill with OM to help mark out something called arenas. She marched about the field trailing a long piece of string and carrying little white pegs and a hammer. It was rather fun to run through the string so making it follow me like a snake, and the pegs were good chewing material - I wonder why I was shut in the car? I was disappointed to be left in the kitchen for much of the day of the competition, but in the afternoon OM came for me and we went up to the big field where we found lots of strange people, horses, lorries and cars. The smart lead you bought me had been left behind, so OM attached me to a piece of pale blue baling string which looked quite fetching against my

Blenheim colouring. I kept close to OM so that I should not be trodden on. Humans and horses all appeared rather damp and muddy and a fine rain swept across; perhaps I had been well placed in the warm kitchen. I assisted in the prize giving when there was much calling out of names and coloured ribbons were given out. Your young sister was given a ribbon and a small silver cup - it did not look as though it would hold much breakfast. Several photographs were taken of Me and I was admired by many; I waved my tail gently whenever there was clapping, some of this applause was plainly directed my way.

I believe we return to the main home soon. I'm looking forward to the drive back and hope I'll be given more chocolate on the way.

Love and licks, Florrie.

OM attached me to a piece of pale blue baling string ...

One is high, one can see, one can be seen

NOTE. Looking back over these outpourings of my youth, I am struck by the perception I showed in being immediately enthusiastic about travel by lorry. For a small dog it has many advantages. One is high, one can see, one can be seen. Another great bonus is that progress is steady and smooth. I have found, especially when driven in small cars by Young Mistress, the motion is somewhat bounding, and you never quite know when you may have to cling on by your toe nails to maintain your position on the seat. I have heard OM claim that with horses behind you the driver should be able to balance a glass of water on the dashboard. Of course I know the stupid things fall over very easily, and are always damaging themselves and have to be wrapped in many sorts of protective covering at every turn. However, this does mean the accompanying dog can sit up, lie down or stand up and bark, confident that one will not be unexpectedly tipped onto one's nose and this adds greatly to the comfort of one's journey.

Back at base
September

Dear Young Mistress,

We are safely back and I have cleared the front and back lawns of some bold birds and a squirrel - the cheek of these creatures making free of the place in my absence!

A big surprise last week - OM went out with the Master and they did not take me. However it was a hot day and they probably thought I was better suited to lie under the trees, keeping an eye open for the odd blackbird. Back they came in the afternoon with a *black puppy* of the *Labrador* breed - I am not sure whether to be pleased or displeased. She is of course very young, a mere eight weeks, amiable and good natured and, like most of her breed, rather simple minded. Old Nicky was very welcoming to her; I was more circumspect. She whines a lot - larger dogs have little restraint - and has already totally devoured a bone that I had been quietly meditating on for several days past. I can see I shall have to look to my own, though I daresay there will be advantages, such as another warm friendly presence in the bed at night, and I do not think she will be a danger to my established first claim on the laps in the evenings; I was relieved to hear OM say that a Labrador is *not* a lapdog.

As time passes I can see my position is under no threat from Hera - so the puppy has been named. She obviously recognises my innate superiority with regard to brain power, and I am able to acknowledge that she does have some ability with her nose; I foresee we may be able to work the hedges and undergrowth together fruitfully. I have some respect for her destructive power. I don't think OM was best pleased when she found the leg of one of the kitchen stools chewed through to breaking point during the night, but this does mean that I can leave to Hera the task of softening a chew or grinding down a bone - difficult work for my small jaw. Cavaliers have over many generations become used to choice morsels and find the rougher stuff hard going. In all I think she will make a useful companion and that we shall rub along together well enough.

Looking forward to seeing you at the weekend,

Love from Florrie.

I don't think OM was best pleased when she found the leg of one of the stools chewed through to breaking point

Chalk Hill
October

Dear Young Mistress,

Today I had a great success! We were passing through one of the fields, just nosing around, when I glimpsed a little movement. Without hesitation I pounced, pushing my nose deep into the clump of grass before me - a snap with my jaws, and I found I had caught my first mouse! I held it proudly up, and wondered whether I should at once eat it. I was a bit relieved when OM came up and took it away. She made much of me, Hera was most impressed and we spent several more minutes sniffing through the grass and trying practice pounces, but although there were good smells we didn't find any more live prey.

Quite often I go shopping in the car with OM. I always make myself comfortable on her seat when she leaves me, it's pleasantly warm and of course is the right place for the dog in charge to lie. I was insulted to find recently that a *dog gate* had been installed in her Saab, and that she actually expected Hera and me to remain cramped up in the very back of the vehicle behind this obstruction. I could see some sense in restraining Hera in this way, because OM placed a large box of groceries on the further side of the barrier and then went off again. As I have mentioned, a young Labrador has the capacity for quick destruction and consumption, but I am now old enough to understand correct behaviour. I no longer chew through paper packages, I wait for my meals to be properly served up and I will not put up with uncomfortable imprisonment behind such a barrier. Immediately I found myself in this situation I assessed the possibilities and found I could easily slip through the small gap at the side. OM was a little surprised to find me as usual on her seat when she returned, but I think appreciates my feelings. She now puts the groceries *behind* the dog gate; I remain in front and Hera can stretch out on the back seat.

Ever your loving Florrie.

I should record at this point the passing of my first Christmas, which I found a very enjoyable time. Young Mistress came home for a few days, and various human relatives came to stay, some bringing their dogs which included a couple more dachshunds and a strange little animal that could hardly be seen for hair, who told me she was of the Shih-tzu breed and was a very self possessed young lady. There was much rustling of paper and unwrapping of parcels - we dogs had some extra biscuits, quite unnecessarily done up in coloured paper. For several days after Christmas, the breakfasts included a good proportion of turkey, a flavour I like and wish was on the menu more frequently.

After New Year, Young Mistress took me with her to London for a short stay.

EVER YOUR AFFECTIONATE

Parson's Green
January

Dear Old Mistress,

This is a very noisy place and the petrol smells are dreadful. The house of Young Mistress is all right, but one just *has* to sit on the sofa downstairs because the floors are covered with bits of paper, boxes, shoes, books, newspapers and other objects - while upstairs more shoes and pieces of clothing strewn around the floor make the bed the obvious place for a dog requiring a little relaxation from the hubbub of London life.

... upstairs more shoes and pieces of clothing strewn around the floor make the bed the obvious place for a dog requiring a little relaxation

Sanitary arrangements are strange - I have to be put on my lead and march along a hard pavement until we reach a small area of grass. There my nose tells me very many other dogs of all sorts have been before me - it is really a bit public - but I take a very careful sniff around and finally select a place on which to perform that I hope has not been contaminated by too many inferior breeds. YM then takes out a shovel and bag and clears up; it is evident this is not done by all other dog walkers. Traces of other dogs are always interesting and I like to investigate them thoroughly, but there is such a thing as an *embarras de richesse*, as quite a decent little poodle I met yesterday remarked to me. I certainly miss my spacious lawns at Chalk Hill. YM has been at home most of the time, and although the music she puts on is sometimes a little loud, in this new environment it is good to have her around. I find it a trifle worrying to be left in charge alone, though I try to keep my self possession and not to show too much relief - just a pleasant welcome back - when she returns.

In the evenings I have had a new experience. I have been to the pub! Again it is rather noisy, but I suppose the smell of beer, smoke and humans is slightly better than petrol. I have received a lot of attention and have been very much admired. I sit close by YM, holding my head high, gently waving my tail and meditating on my Royal antecedents. Quite often I am offered a crisp, a peanut - or once, and far the best - a small piece of a meat pie. I accept these gifts graciously, but if the flavour is not to my liking - and some of the crisps taste very odd - I wait until the donor's attention is elsewhere before rejecting the item and placing it unobtrusively under YM's stool.

My best wishes to Hera - I do not think Fulham would suit her.

Love from Florrie.

Chalk Hill
February

Dear Young Mistress,

It was most interesting to experience a different lifestyle. However I am quite pleased to be back in the country with OM, though I was rather sick on the first morning after my return: possibly that Brie from the leftover ploughman's I consumed the previous evening at the Black Bear was a little rich. OM has put me on a very plain diet since then. We had a good walk in the woods and fields today when I distinguished myself by putting up a whole covey of partridges. I felt I was truly fulfilling my ancestral duty. Hera, poor fool, tried to run after them long after they were airborne; I simply turned back to the long grass where they had been hiding in case there should be a lone fugitive left. With pheasants this is often the case, with smaller game birds rarely so, but one should always check.

... putting up a whole covey of partridges

I am beginning to nose out smells of young birds in several of the bushes and trees in the garden. I have to keep my finds secret from OM; she did not seem to approve when she found me doing my best to reach up into the hazel bushes where I had located some thrush fledglings only just above my head. She made a rude comparison with a cat, so I gave her the cold shoulder that evening and did not allow her the comfort of me on her lap after supper. She has shut the gate down to the lower part of the garden too, very frustrating.

Ever your loving Florrie.

Chalk Hill
June, my second year

Dear Young Mistress,

I have just had a most exhilarating experience - I have performed in a play and been acclaimed by all! It came about because the school which your young sister attends required an intelligent dog to take an important part in their summer production. The first intimation I had of some unusual happening was being subjected to a full bath in the back sink. I endure being washed, I accept it as inevitable - but difficult to understand - when I have rolled in a particularly fruity corpse, but this time I was simply immersed by OM for no apparent reason. Mind you, since she has taken to using her own shower attachment on the taps, it *is* better than having to stand ankle deep in tepid water while being splashed about with a sponge, also I quite like the herb shampoo she's used lately. Anyhow, I put up with this ordeal - conditioner as well and then the hot air puffer really did make it an ordeal - and off we set to Monksholme, a drive with which I am familiar as I have accompanied OM there a couple of times this summer.

*Your young sister wore a shiny frock and had a couple
of long and very dead furry animals around her neck ...*

On arrival I was taken for an agreeable walk in the spacious grounds, where I noticed the usual rural smells were overlaid by a tinge of leather and human feet. I had a good look round before being taken into a small room in a tall building where we found your young sister with a number of other rather excited young people. I was welcomed warmly, OM left me, and I sat watching while they fussed around with their clothes and smeared some coloured stuff on their faces. Your young sister wore a shiny frock and had a couple of long and very dead furry animals hung round her neck; they smelt of mothballs. Finally she gave me an encouraging pat, picked me up and carried me out of the door. Suddenly I found myself in a huge high room, faced with many bright dazzling lights. As I became used to the glare I realised there were large numbers of humans sitting beyond the lights - rows of them stretching upwards - and they were all looking at Me!

We were out there for a long time, and I am still not quite sure what was supposed to be going on.* Some half dozen or so youngsters appeared to have got their accommodation for a weekend in a muddle. Your young sister spoke loudly in an unfamiliar way, it reminded me a little of the poodle acquaintance I made on Parson's Green. They all talked a lot. The gist of it seemed to be that there was one room with one bed and both your young sister and some unknown man were laying claim to it. I do not myself like to share a bed with a stranger, but I thought he could have been allowed to curl up in a corner. While these arguments took place, I was either placed upon my temporary mistress's lap, or sat beside her chair. In whichever position I found myself, I kept my eyes on my audience and gently waved my tail. I was a little shocked when other voices joined in the debate about sleeping arrangements and I came to understand that my mistress's claim on the bed was conditional upon me being confined to some *shed.* To her credit she was voluble in her objections to this insulting stipulation, but some other strange man strode up and took hold of me in such a rough manner that I was impelled to give a very sharp yelp. There was tremendous applause as I was carried out!

I then rested comfortably on a pile of discarded clothes and was fed several sweet biscuits of the sort OM does not allow me. I heard the voices and arguments continue at a distance, and there was much laughter and clapping. A little later your young sister rushed in, plucked me up and I accompanied her and all the cast - as I have learnt they are called - in front of the bright lights again, where we received much cheering and clapping. I waved my tail as graciously as I could while being somewhat smothered by the dead furry animals. I had a better opportunity to speak with my numerous admirers as I passed through their ranks on my way out with OM. A path was cleared for me, I bowed to left and right, pausing to receive caresses and pats while OM answered various questions, such as how old I was and how often I had performed in public before. There was general amazement that this was my debut and I was much complimented on my poise and *sang-froid.*

* 'A Cuckoo in the Nest' - Ben Travers

I have been telling Hera of my brush with the bright lights of the theatrical world. She, poor dear, would not relish such an experience. OM has been looking at me in a speculative way, and muttering about cashing in on that natural ability to show off, and what about advertising Pal or Pedigree Chum. She well knows I very much prefer those select and expensive little tins of another brand.

Ever your affectionate, Florrie.

Shortly after this glimpse of stardom, supplies for horses and humans were again gathered together, and we set off for my second long summer holidays on Exmoor. I was by now well past my first birthday, and able to enjoy proper walks on the farm and moor. Hera went out with the horses most days and in any weather - I suppose it is the calling of one of her breed to be impervious to the discomforts of wind and rain and to accompany their human under unpleasant conditions. She showed a positive enthusiasm for wet places, and indeed needed no encouragement to spring into the river; I was very relieved that OM shut her into a stable when she returned soaking wet from her excursions rather than letting her drip into our bed. It was, I believe, a particularly inclement August. For myself a stroll along the edge of the river does very well, and if I am required to cross some minor stream, I quickly assess the lie of the land and search out a spot where I can jump lightly from bank to bank. Should the width be beyond my capabilities, I wait to be lifted over.

... needed no encouragement to spring into the river

We returned to Chalk Hill where the horses continued to take up what seemed to me to be a disproportionate amount of everyone's time, though I enjoyed the rides in the lorry to competitive outings. On one of these Young Mistress's horse made a particularly stupid mistake - instead of jumping cleanly, as I have to acknowledge he usually did, he tumbled over the obstacle so causing my Young Mistress a heavy fall on to her head. Initially she seemed not much the worse for this mishap, but as the weeks went by it became clear that her London occupation was inappropriate for the time being. How it came about I am not sure, but during the following winter I accompanied her down the familiar Exmoor route, although our final destination was a place unknown to me, and one where I would encounter new experiences and challenges.

Litton
February

Dear Old Mistress,

I find myself in new and very stimulating surroundings. YM appears to have taken on a small farm, and my support is much needed to help her keep the assorted animal population in order.

... to have taken on a small farm

We have a quantity of what are known as tame lambs - these are lambs with no mother, so they require frequent feeds from bottles and we often go out during the night to administer these. Some of the lambs are very silly and show little gratitude or appreciation of this sustenance. Recently YM has acquired two strong smelling animals called goats, and some of the more sensible lambs are now feeding from one of these goats. The other goat does not wish to let the lambs feed and a good deal of scuffling and sharp words take place. I am a little wary of her pointed hooves but I give a bark or two from a safe distance if I think it called for. What I find much more interesting than these feeding activities is the strong scent of rodents that permeates all the sheds. I have always been a keen mouser with one or two kills to my credit, but there is something more powerful than mouse in the wind here.

It is very cold inside and outside. There is little heating in the house but I must not complain; the interesting smells, which are in the house as well as the buildings, keep me constantly on patrol. Also YM has made me a smart coat, of quilted blue fabric bound in scarlet. I had previously thought poorly of dressed up dogs, but I have to confess this outfit adds considerably to my comfort. I know you do

YM has made me a smart coat ...

not generally approve of dogs on beds, human beds that is, but under the circumstances here I think you will be relieved to know that YM and I curl up together for mutual warmth and prevention of frostbite at night. I myself do not hurry to leave the bed in the morning.

Ever your affectionate, Florrie.

Litton
March

Dear Old Mistress,

The weather has become a trifle warmer and YM is having a wood burning heater installed, so perhaps some of the radiators will start to work. I notice that before the lights can be made to function, YM goes off to a black and evil smelling shed and heaves about beside a oily machine until there is a loud chugging noise. This machine is a generator; it is not always possible to start it and sometimes it runs out of whatever it eats, so quite often we have candlelight. Still the days are lengthening and those stupid lambs are a bit more self sufficient.

We now have hens: every time YM and I go out in the car we seem to return with two or three more of a different kind. I did find it almost intolerable when a clutch of chicks was brought *into the house* and their run placed in the kitchen with a warm light suspended over it. They darted about, cheeping away; I sat contemplating them and was assessing how many I could seize in one quick foray when I felt YM take hold of my scruff and she spoke very severely. It is apparent they have to be put up with.

... a clutch of chicks was brought into the house

It is convenient that your Exmoor house is but a short drive downhill from here. YM visits it when the hot water fails and she wishes to do some washing; it is quite pleasant to feel carpet under one's feet once more. However, once home again, the minor discomforts of Litton are forgotten as I pad around its numerous barns and sheds, investigating the very interesting smells and traces of varied wildlife that are to be found there.

Your affectionate Florrie.

P.S. My coat is growing noticeably thicker.

Litton
April

Dear Old Mistress,

My hour of glory came - *I have killed a rat!* I do not believe that many contemporary Cavaliers can boast of this achievement - our jaws are said by some to be impracticably short, but I assure you that I seized the little monster, whom I detected creeping about in the shed adjoining the kitchen, by the neck, shook it with all my might and very soon it went quite limp.

YM, hearing my battle growl, came quickly to my side, dissuaded me from dining on my prey (I have to confess I had no great wish to do so) and praised me quite extravagantly. I feel a trifle offended that she has just arranged for the pest officer from the Council to visit, but now I have the experience to identify that rodent smell more exactly, I realise the rats are plentiful so I should not grudge this man his opportunity of taking part in their extermination.

I have killed a rat!

35

Later: the pest man came and went about his task in a very tame way, just putting little packets about in corners of some of the buildings, from which I was then excluded. It appears they are poison - I thought we might have more of a chase in which I could take part and display my expertise; all rather disappointing.

Your affectionate rat conquering Florrie.

Litton
May

Dear Old Mistress,

Those hens are multiplying all over the place. We have several very small sheds with wire runs set up in the yards, and they each contain a mother hen and a number of chicks. Occasionally a chick escapes, and I have been strictly forbidden to help in its capture. When YM leaves me in charge, as she does from time to time, she allows me a free run - of course by now I understand the limits of our territory and can be trusted to remain within them without restraint. Recently I was sitting taking the air on the doorstep - when the view is not obscured by fog or driving rain as can often happen on these heights, it is a magnificent one and worthy of contemplation. Suddenly my eye was caught by a movement on the opposite side of the yard, and I beheld a reddish brown creature come stealthily through the gate. I barked my gruffest bark, which brought it to a halt, and I was able to observe that the creature was quite dog like, but with a very full tail and a very strong smell. Its eyes met mine, our gazes locked - but a Cavalier can stare with a disdainful grandeur that few other animals can withstand, and the thing soon slunk away.

Following some words with the collie who patrols the adjacent fields, I understand this was a fox, and that this species is extremely partial to hens of all sorts. As I myself am forbidden to have sport among these birds, I have resolved to adopt a fierce and aggressive pose the next time that bold creature puts its black nose round the gate. The collie assures me they are not difficult to deter, and will not persist in their larcenous activities once they have been detected. I thought it wise to take advice - foxes are obviously larger than me, and the teeth looked sharp and well polished.

Ever your affectionate, Florrie.

I beheld a reddish brown creature come stealthily through the gate

Litton
Summer, my third year

Dear Old Mistress,

I enjoyed my stay with you down the road while YM was absent for a time, and to have had the opportunity to tell Hera and old Nicky something of the real life that takes place away from their sheltered surroundings. A pity all those hens had to come too, but at least I felt a lightening of my responsibilities, no foxes dare to venture so close to your establishment as they do to our more isolated hill top.

Here recently I have had to take a very positive stance with the cheeky beasts; there are two or three really brazen specimens that lurk about our boundaries, and a short sprint is required, followed up by a barked stream of abuse to shift them any distance. At least all the chicks are now grown, and thank goodness several have been placed in cardboard boxes and driven away to new homes. We still have a fair flock of those fluffy white ones and some rather imposing large black ones, which are feathered from their red top bits right down to the ground. I treat this latter breed with some respect, they are taller than me.

... fluffy white ones and some rather imposing large black ones

YM has been to one or two local markets lately, and I am apprehensive that a horse may be added to our establishment. I overheard a lot of talk about a 'recently backed four year old full of promise' that sounded a bit ominous, and there has been a telephone conversation or two on similar lines.

Affectionately, Florrie.

... and I ride in style

Litton
Summer

Dear Old Mistress,

I was pleased to see you and the lorry last week, and most relieved when that sensible mare Hwin was unloaded. She at least understands her place, moves carefully around her stable and is not given to sudden unexpected darting about. Her arrival has meant we go together for quite long excursions over the moor. Where the hills are steep, or the heather is overgrown and becomes an inconvenient height for my progress, or where we encounter particularly wet ground, YM takes me up in front of her - she keeps a folded blanket on the saddle for my comfort, and I ride in style.

It is a great pleasure to be able to view my surroundings from such a commanding position. My experience of horses is sufficient to doubt whether I could have enjoyed this pleasing new experience from the back of a four year old; I am glad to report that we have heard no more of this possible acquisition.

Those wretched hens are still present, but I believe the adult sheep now occupying our larger field belong to our neighbour - his collie appears to have the responsibility of keeping them in order, and I approve this arrangement. I never felt controlling bleating young lambs was quite the proper task for a Cavalier - sheep are best left to the artisan class.

I do like helping YM in the garden, where she has been very busy and has made some colourful little patches around the back steps. I sit and meditate on the top step as she digs around, all the while keeping an alert eye and nose ready to detect movements among the local wildlife. The rats have not been sighted or smelt lately, but there are plenty of mice to provide sport, and the foxes look in more frequently than I think proper.

Ever your affectionate, Florrie.

Litton
September

Dear Old Mistress,

YM has called in the professionals again! She was much angered by an especially determined fox breaking into the pen of a particularly rare and expensive fowl - only a few feathers were found in the morning and I have to confess I was too well wound up in the duvet to hear any sound of disturbance during the night. It is becoming colder and one has to take care - my coat is not yet of winter weight.

A few days after this dastardly theft, quite early in the morning, there was the sound of something not unlike the noises YM's brother makes on his trumpet and a clatter of horses' hooves. I took up my favourite stance on the top step as a pack of foxhounds surged into our bigger yard accompanied by a couple of mounted men wearing rather faded red coats. I do not think I resemble a fox but such a number of large hounds might make a mistake, and I was glad to be well above them and to have YM at my side.

Away they went across our fields ...

YM spoke to one of the men - she was able to give quite an accurate account of the route usually taken by the Litton foxes, though of course I could have been even more precise. However it was not my impression that those hulking great hounds used much forethought, or were inclined to seek advice. Away they went across our fields and were soon pushing around in our boundary hedge. Suddenly one of them started yelling in an over excited manner, the rest joined in - I've never heard such a din! It obviously upset Hwin who dashed round and round her stable in a very uncharacteristic way, straining to see out of the half door every so often. I confess I felt quite stirred up myself, and when I saw one of our foxes running towards the moor at a greater speed than I'd ever seen him employ, with hounds screaming their heads off after him, I wanted to go too - but YM restrained me.

I'm afraid they failed to catch up with the cunning creature, but I heard them hunting around the neighbourhood during the morning and there's no doubt they made it clear it was healthier for him not to hang around our premises - I haven't seen that sharp black nose come round the yard gate for a few days.

Affectionately, Florrie.

Litton
October

Dear Old Mistress,

I was surprised when we called on you while you were staying down the hill last week to find a tri-colour Cavalier puppy in residence. I appreciate how much you must miss my constant company now my duties call me to YM's side, but I do visit quite often, so I was a little put out to discover Another in my place at your home. However she seems a good natured little thing and to know her place. I am not keen on sharing my bed except under extreme pressure, and I would prefer not to be expected to make Nell (a somewhat commonplace name for a Cavalier, do you not think?) welcome on my personal bean bag. I am prepared to show her how to cross Exmoor, though I think at present she is a trifle young for such testing ground, and as she was carried for much of the time we walked on the Common, I assume you share my views. Fortunately Hera appears to positively enjoy the company of the very young; maternal instinct is something I can do without - my independence is very important to me.

I am not keen on sharing my bed

Rather to my relief, YM is keeping herself busy in the kitchen - constant use of the cooker does help raise the temperature of that room and counteracts the fresh breeze that blows through. She has also taken to cooking for others at a hotel a little way from here. I generally accompany her and find the few miles drive quite exhilarating. YM speeds down the valley at a good rate, though occasionally we have to brake rather sharply when an unexpected hazard is encountered round one of the many twisting bends. I am becoming quite expert at maintaining my balance - by careful observation of our progress I can often correctly anticipate an emergency stop and brace myself in readiness, so avoiding the undignified tumble forward onto the floor of the car. The position I really prefer is on YM's lap; I notice you do not approve of this, but it is a comforting place to be when I have had a particularly long wait by myself in the car. I do not understand why I am not allowed to accompany YM to the hotel kitchen - I am very good at keeping out of the way and quick to pick up any crumbs that fall to the floor; however I am visited from time to time and provided with a hot water bottle when the weather is chilly.

All this culinary activity means less time for agricultural pursuits, though a fair number of those tedious hens still squawk around the yards. I am hopeful there will not be a repetition of the tame lamb enterprise - really rather unpleasant having to leave one's warm bed at night to feed the ungrateful little beasts.

Ever your affectionate, Florrie.

Litton
January

Dear Old Mistress,

My third Christmas is behind me! We had a very happy time with you, and I am most appreciative of my new dog bed. As you evidently had observed, my old one was always rather thin on filling - a more abundant layer of beads between me and the floor is a great improvement, while the chestnut shades in the cover pattern match my coat perfectly. I was amazed to find that Nell had grown a lot larger, and is perhaps a little *lanky* at present; she certainly runs very fast, more like a whippet than a dignified Cavalier. Her coat though silky lacks substance - I am pleased to report that my own has become exceedingly thick and I have a substantial ruff around my neck. This winter nature is looking after me and I do not think I shall need my padded jacket. A recent visitor told YM that she had only once seen a coat to compare with mine, and this was on a Cavalier from the north of a place called Norway.

Our cooking trips continue; though when they are made twice daily - lunch and dinner - I prefer to remain on guard here, usually during the evening run. The weather is steadily getting colder, so I curl up on my new bed which is placed close to a radiator, which occasionally is warm, and await the return of YM. Once she is back and we have checked the hens, we go up to her bedroom, YM puts on a different and thicker set of clothes and we settle down under duvet and extra blankets.

Affectionately, Florrie.

Litton
February

Dear Old Mistress,

How fortunate you and the Master were at your place down the hill last week! YM and I have together coped with many different problems and challenges during the past year, but I did not find it comfortable - and YM was rather nonplussed - when water began pouring at a considerable rate through the kitchen ceiling. I noticed it made its way with particular force down either end of the strip light, and quite soon I was up to my ankles. This house is not ever very warm but has previously provided quite adequate shelter from the rain, however heavily it falls. It was late evening, and the fog very dense, even by Litton standards. YM rushed around, looking in corners and cupboards in a quite desperate way and muttering about stopcocks. This searching did not change the situation and soon I heard her telephoning to the Master; luckily you had not yet left for your dinner party - and we were both very relieved when, some little time later, we heard his tread come across the yard. The drive had been totally blocked with snow for a week or so and I understand he had had a difficult walk through the fields, wasting time when he was incorrectly diverted by our neighbour's lights. Some human senses are woefully inadequate, had I been with him I would of course have led him directly here. However it was a particularly disagreeable night, and possibly to be indoors, even though by now the water was above my knees, was preferable to being outside.

The drive had been totally blocked with snow for a week or so

More searching began - made easier by the light of Master's torch - ours had faded away - and eventually a tap was found in a dark corner of one of the barns which when turned slowed the flow through the ceiling. Some mopping up operations were undertaken, my bed placed to dry by the stove and a few buckets set under any persistent drips. In other rooms the carpeting felt unpleasantly damp; I was glad when we abandoned the house, crossed the fields without mishap, found YM's car which lately she has been leaving beyond the snow drifts, and were soon down in the Royal Oak, where good fires burn and real warmth exists! Here my wet legs and underparts dried quickly; I curled up discreetly under the table, and YM slipped me several pieces of steak.

I was pleased to spend the rest of the night in your household. Those unworldly dogs Hera and Nell were surprised by my arrival, but I was too sleepy to recount many of the details for their enlightenment.

Now the weather has improved and we are gradually drying out. A man from the insurance came to look at the carpets - and the kitchen ceiling, a part of which has fallen on the floor.

Ever your affectionate, Florrie.

Litton
April

Dear Old Mistress,

It was agreeable to spend a few days with you while YM went off on an excursion to even greater heights than Exmoor - I understand to slide down snow covered hills balanced on some sort of elongated footwear. One would have thought she had had enough of such conditions last winter, but she has returned brown in the face and most cheerful.

I was surprised to find that you have increased the dog population yet again! Indeed I had observed that old Nicky is failing fast and hardly ever leaves her place by the Aga except when food is on offer, but I would find just two other dogs plenty of company when I am with you. I cannot be too critical of your choice as you tell me the new Cavalier puppy is a near relation of mine - a half sister in fact - though I do not recall that I was ever such an insipid sandy colour, and she has not many patches of *that*, too much white altogether, I fear. No sign of a lozenge mark either. I acknowledge she has a keen nose for one so young - she led us to the dead crow under the holly bush in the front field without hesitation, even though it was lying upwind. Really Daisy is *not* a very distinguished name for one of our breed and she shows little sign of recognising it, or for that matter of responding to any human calls. You describe her as fey - whatever that may mean - but I think she carries the general independence of the Cavalier beyond the acceptable, and is plain disobedient by nature. That uncritical and simple Nell has no reservations about extending the paw of friendship, and I expect will enjoy the companionship of another young thing. Please note three on a lap do not fit comfortably; as I grow older I find two quite a crowd and my preference is to curl up in sole and undisturbed possession.

I believe I can now safely report there are no tame lambs to be cared for this spring. The assorted poultry unfortunately survived the

... three on a lap do not fit comfortably

care of the neighbour during our absence and YM is still cooking for others, but we are at present making only one journey a day for this purpose. We have had visitors at the weekends, one in particular is of note; I find myself quite drawn to him, though he is somewhat unpredictable, also a trifle noisy - but then his ringing tones are preferable to those cackling hens and crowing cocks. He certainly brings sparkle and fun to all we do during his stay - YM seems to feel this too.

Ever your affectionate, Florrie.

The days lengthened, and my coat began its change from winter weight to summer. OM complains how long this process lasts, but I am relieved it is not more rapid - I like to have an adequate layer left for cold May winds. The Man with the Loud Voice came to stay several more times, and we had some good outings. I noticed the back of his car contained a quantity of oily smelling tools, as well as lots of plastic and metal objects - the sort of thing that the Master says will come in useful and takes off to his workroom when he finds OM putting them in the dustbin. In between our excursions and walks, he helped YM mend a couple of hen runs, prevented water running down a wall, which had been happening even when it wasn't raining, and did something to YM's car which stopped it going quite so jerkily. He seemed a useful person to have around, though there were times when I sensed a lack of respect for my position and a readiness to suggest I should be displaced from lap or sofa, or left behind when a trip to the pub was proposed, which I did not find acceptable.

I made a last sortie through the enticing and always interesting barns ...

Quite suddenly - and life with YM accustoms one to sudden changes - it seemed we were leaving Litton. Our days were filled with clearing up and packing up, trips to dispose of equipment and livestock, including a number of those birds, and I made a last sortie through the enticing and always interesting barns and sheds.

Finally the remaining birds, still numerous, were placed in more cardboard boxes and crammed into YM's car, leaving little room for me. I had to crouch between the gear lever and a carton containing a large Cochin cockerel, so travelling in considerable discomfort; my frequent requests to come on YM's lap were refused as this was a long journey on motorway roads, and it was a great relief to arrive at last back to base with OM. She was not especially pleased to receive additional poultry, but later I heard her say privately to the Master that they were a small price to pay for the relief of having YM off that isolated rock.

We spent a few weeks in the comfortable and predictable surroundings of the main home. During this time my young sister Daisy met with a sad accident. We had just accompanied OM across the front field to open the gate and allow that shaggy old pony Melrose to pass through and graze in the further field. He had hurried through to do this - the grass is indeed greener there - when one of the stabled horses called in that hysterical way they have. Melrose then made another and quite unexpected rush back through the open gate. Daisy, who was pottering along rather to the rear, chanced to be in his way and was struck by one of his hooves. She cried out dreadfully. We all sped to the rescue and OM soon wrapped her in blankets and set off to the Vet. She did look very seedy, and from my experience of life and death at Litton I was prepared for OM to come home alone. However I have to acknowledge my young sister has tenacity - she returned, to be laid by the Aga on cushions, surrounded by hot water bottles, fed frequent little sips of milk and glucose - for which she was always ready - and survived this traumatic experience, though unfortunately not unscathed.

Her tail now droops limply; it does not wave and - worse - it cannot be carried in that proud flag flying manner proper to a Cavalier. The relief that she was mobile and that her hind legs were unaffected has, I believe, led OM and the Master to underrate the disadvantage of a handicapped tail. After several days, or indeed

... laid by the Aga on cushions, surrounded by hot water bottles

weeks, of very preferential treatment, she made, apart from the tail, a good recovery. Nell played boisterous games with her regardless of her injuries and altered aspect - the Master said these were good physiotherapy; I of course put away such puppyish activities long ago. The other-worldly air that has always hung about Daisy perhaps deepened - her brush with the Next World or increasing maturity?

OM said Melrose never did take much notice of anything in his path, once he had set off on one of his wild surges, and that in his younger days he gave her several worrying moments as, when ridden by my Young Mistress, he swept after hounds regardless of other riders and pretty regardless of the efforts made by Young Mistress to restrain him.

In spite of the home comforts I found that I missed my status as Only Dog. The companionship of my own kind is not essential to my well-being. When relegated to my beanbag rather than YM's bed, I certainly like to have it to myself. The risk of some junior relation wishing to share it is undesirable. However, once more a change of lifestyle was imminent; With little warning, a quick packing of suitcases took place and one afternoon YM and I whirled off to London.

Clapham
Summer, my fourth year

Dear Old Mistress,

We have joined the Man with the Loud Voice in his London house! As you know, my experience of city life is limited but I am confident I shall adapt myself to the very different challenges now set before me. Perhaps the chief of these is the Man with the Loud Voice himself - he is plainly unsure whether my presence is really necessary, and I have heard mention of 'happier in the country' and 'London is no place for a dog' - this latter quite untrue, I note dogs everywhere. I am sure I shall, with the exercise of charm and tact, soon win him over.

I am gradually learning the limits of my new territory; at the front of the house is street - that means traffic so I am discouraged from going

... in his London house

that way; at the back is a small garden which has possibilities, for I have discovered that I am able to enter the next door gardens on either side through convenient holes in the fence. While exploring the very overgrown piece to our right yesterday, I followed a well trodden path through the willow herb. I could see this ended in a little patch of sun, and I had in mind taking a short nap - the late hours kept by young people are rather disturbing. Picture my reaction when, on reaching the sunny place, I found myself eyeball to eyeball with a large black cat! To date I have had scant experience of this species, and I was not entirely sure how to handle the encounter. Instinct told me I should adopt an aggressive pose, yet as a newcomer I wondered if co-existence was the custom. The cat had no doubts; it fluffed out its fur, doubling its size and hissed horribly.

... eyeball to eyeball with a large black cat!

At the same moment, YM, leaning from a window above and seeing all, gave a hunting cry of the sort she would use when encouraging me to pursue small game at Litton. My course was clear - I sprang forwards, barking furiously; the cat with amazing dexterity leapt vertically up the fence and with another jump gained the roof next door. I now appreciate some good sport is available in London, and I spent the next couple of hours checking all the gardens I could reach for cats. Eventually I heard YM calling from afar and had problems finding my way back; indeed she had to climb over several of the neighbours' fences to reach me and was not best pleased.

Ever your affectionate, Florrie.

Clapham
August

Dear Old Mistress,

I am now well oriented as to my outside territory, and the cats of the area have learned to keep their proper distance. Inside I am still a little confused about the various occupants and their activities. YM goes off most lunch times, when she cooks for others - very fortunate others to judge by the unmistakable aroma of smoked salmon that I can often detect, and also by the occasional delicious leftovers that come back for supper. The Man with the Loud Voice sometimes goes off too in his car full of tools, but he comes back smelling of brick dust, cement and drains. More frequently he stays with me - he is becoming quite reconciled to my company - and he generally spends the time knocking down a part of the house.

I do wonder what he is searching for - the latest project is to dig a very large and very deep hole in the floor of what I have heard called the kitchen - though what cooking YM undertakes does not take place there. At present she has the cooker on the landing and washes up in the bath. Anyhow, the Man with the Loud Voice has decreed the hole is to be a metre square. I

... I watch with great interest

watch with great interest - but so far the excavation has yielded nothing of note, just a growing heap of dust, broken brick and stone - no hint of bones. Perhaps he has buried some particular treasure and cannot remember where?

Also living here is the Tall Fair Man, his Tired Girlfriend and the Thick Dark Man. The poor Tired Girlfriend teaches little children all day - she returns smelling of chalk, toffees and torn paper and goes off to bed early each evening. The Tall Fair Man sometimes sets off carrying cameras and sometimes stays to help the latest pulling down, while the Thick Dark Man either accompanies the Man with the Loud Voice when he goes out in the car or joins the assaults on the house.

Ever your affectionate, Florrie.

Clapham
September

Dear Old Mistress,

I have been trying a wonderful new sport; when digging is over for the day the Man with the Loud Voice picks me up and takes me down the street. Once there he conceals me under his capacious coat until we spy a cat; I am then quickly put down and with a cry of 'go to, Bonzo' I rush after the enemy who, taken by surprise, flees for refuge to some high place in a tree or on a wall. We only indulge ourselves in this way occasionally because YM does not wholly approve, but there is not much traffic at that time and I have learnt to curtail my barking to avoid the risk of attracting the neighbours or owners of the cats. Indeed I have decided the Man with the Loud Voice is the Man I Love - by who else would I tolerate being addressed as Bonzo?

I am disappointed to report that the great hole has been filled in with concrete and a brick pillar - most uninteresting. Across the pillar lies a steel girder, apparently to support the ceiling while the Man I Love takes out one of the walls. I am beginning to understand that the purpose of all this activity is improvement and renovation of the house and that one day building up will take the place of pulling down. As yet there is little sign of it. Personally I like the place very much as it is - why put floorboards down and so cover up excellent mouse hunting terrain? The piles of discarded planks and bricks which accumulate in odd corners also provide refuge for spiders and other creepy little things, and I have never despised smaller prey.

However YM has decreed that the rate of work should increase and I note on most days the Man I Love stays in and with the help of the Thick Dark Man has put a construction of poles and boards all round the back of the house. Standing on these boards, they took the roof off the bathroom. As most of the floor has also been removed, YM complained with some justification that she had problems in gaining access to the bath. The Man I Love then announced that the joists were rotten and that the bath might descend into the room below at any time. YM maintained something must be done to provide alternative washing-up and personal washing facilities. How humans do fuss; I lick my plate clean and am only too relieved to be spared the unpleasantness of a bath.

Affectionately, Florrie.

Clapham
October

Dear Old Mistress,

There has been a great gale! I was awakened in the night by a far off but heavy thud; as I opened my eyes I observed it was very much darker than is usual in the city - generally an orange kind of light can be seen from my window throughout the hours of darkness. This was not now present, and the wind was howling in a concentrated sort of way quite unlike the free blasts to which I became accustomed at Litton. Footsteps sounded on the stairs and the Man I Love shouted up to the Thick Dark Man something about the scaffolding blowing away. It is common for the lights in this house to go out, but being dark outside too made it all very black. I could hear strange creaking noises and sensed movement of the whole building; I decided my YM might need my support and comfort, left my beanbag and made a quick dash for the bed. Crashes of falling metal poles close outside the wall caused me to curl myself more deeply into the pillows. There were cries for rope from the men outside, and YM left me briefly to supply this need. Above the terrible noise of the wind I could hear them calling to each other in some excitement, but for once I felt no wish to join in. YM returned, greatly to my relief. More distant thuds, nearer bangs from falling brick and glass, wailing sirens, could all be heard through the roar of the gale; I closed my eyes tightly and wedged myself as far under the duvet and as close to YM as I could.

... trees up which I had chased cats had fallen

Morning - and light - came at last. The wind had died away and most of the scaffolding was still in place, though looking a bit lopsided in places. Out in the street there were many changes - trees up which I had chased cats had fallen, chimney pots lay on the pavement and I had to pick my way carefully over much broken glass. The traffic lights were out of action, but not many cars were about.

We encountered some extreme weather during our Exmoor days, but to be struck in a great city by such a fearsome gale was a most unpleasant experience. I do not understand how the Man I Love could appear to so *relish* it.

Your very affectionate, Florrie.

Clapham
November

Dear Old Mistress,

Works on this house continue and the piles of debris grow higher. YM has several times requested that a skip - whatever that is - should be sent for, but the Man I Love says much of the material can be used again and that it is not yet time.

Sometimes when we have had enough of dust and rubble, we go out for a change of air and alternative exercise to cat chasing. A favourite walk is through Battersea Gardens, where there are lots of birds, some of whom splash about in small ponds which most irritatingly are fenced off. Even if I cannot make them fly, I can have a good bark through the wire. Many other dogs are to be found here - I have discovered complete indifference to their existence is the best reaction to most; it bewilders the would be aggressor and puts the over friendly in their place. Lots of trees blew down in the great gale, and there are good holes for exploration where the roots were torn from the ground - they give an otherwise over-tidy environment a more rural feel.

Recently when I returned from a small solo expedition to a garden three fences away I found the Man I Love staring thoughtfully at the back wall of our house. He inspected it from various angles, then called the Thick Dark Man from the trench he was digging and they consulted together. A decision was reached, and they set about taking it down - the scaffolding was still in place, so they made good progress. By the time YM returned from her lunch cooking, three or four of the rooms had no back wall. I do not think she was very happy with this situation or entirely satisfied by the plastic sheeting slung across in place of the bricks. To divert her mind, they all went to the pub for the evening. I remained on guard, carefully choosing a room with four solid walls and a small fire - winter approaches and it is becoming colder.

Ever your affectionate, Florrie.

*I remained on guard,
carefully choosing a room
with ... a small fire*

Clapham
January

Dear Old Mistress,

I enjoyed our Christmas break with you; it was touching how effusively those young dogs greeted me and how keen they were to hear of my adventures in the great city - what a simple and predictable life they lead.

I have extended my horizons yet again - I have travelled over the sea and visited foreign lands! A sudden resolution was taken to spend the New Year in Scotland, and that very day we set off by car, YM, the Man I Love and the Tall Fair Man. Apparently he is Canadian and his forbears came from the Isle of Skye; while in the pub one evening he told us this several times. We drove all through the night - at least I slept on a lap for most of the journey - but the car seemed to keep going. Looking around me when morning came, I thought the countryside very similar to Exmoor and wondered why we had come so far. However when we at last stopped and I climbed out to stretch my legs the salty air and strong smell of fish was quite different. I looked at the great expanse of water before me with some disquiet, and was uneasy when I understood arrangements were being made for us to take the car on a boat and cross the sea to

Skye. But it was not too bad, just a general feeling of instability and rocking about, and the Isle, when reached, felt quite solid.

Enquiries for somewhere to stay then began, and this proved difficult - others it seemed had also decided to spend Hogmanay - as the natives call it - on Skye, and had made their plans earlier than our party. Eventually we were passed by a helpful man in the Post Office to his second cousin's brother-in-law's wife, whom he said might take us in. This seemed uncertain when this lady perceived me; she stated that her husband would not have a dog in the house. I immediately assumed a attitude of general pleading; sitting beside YM's feet, I waved my tail gently and gave her the sort of look I reserve for begging the rind of an especially choice Camembert. It worked: we were admitted with the proviso that I should remain concealed in the bedroom and would not bark.

Our landlady looked in a couple of times ...

It was now evening, and my young people left to go out for this great celebration. I had my own bed and their luggage so I felt secure that they would return. The noise level outside - our lodgings were close to centre of the little town - soon began to rise, but it all sounded quite cheerful. As time went by it remained cheerful but became somehow rather blurred and a smell similar to that I have noted in pubs but more concentrated drifted in at the window. Our landlady looked in a couple of times, I suspect to check that I was on my own bed - I met her beady glance with a look of slight disdain, conveying, I hoped, surprise that she should doubt my behaviour being anything but entirely correct. By the time she made her second visit, she was more friendly and indeed gave me a biscuit, saying as she went that I was a 'canny wee beastie'. I was not sure how to interpret that. Much later my party came in; they all seemed a little unsteady on their feet and that spirituous smell was strongly marked. I am never in a hurry to rise in the morning, which is fortunate as on the following day breakfast was taken at lunch time.

Some fresh air was considered desirable and we went for an excellent walk beside the sea. Once I had learnt to deal with the unpredictable way the water would suddenly rush in after me, and this I did by keeping well to the rocks where I found many delicious fishy scraps, I enjoyed these new surroundings. As we went further - the Man I Love goes for long walks once he starts - the sea came closer and it was necessary for us all to climb over the rocks. As I sprang easily from one wet boulder to another, many of which were much taller than myself, I was conscious of the advantages of travelling on four legs - the humans stumbled about behind me in a sorry way - and when we gained a stretch of open sand, the wind blew my splendid thick tail just like the sail of a boat, rushing me forwards so that again I easily outdistanced my followers. We took a rest in a sheltered place, and a flask of what I now know to be whisky was passed round; I was given a lick from the lid - a most fiery taste, rather agreeable! The sun came out as we sat there, and I found no difficulty is joining the general wish to take a short nap before the homeward trek.

Now we are back in the great city; it is much colder here than in Scotland, but I have been busy helping the Man I Love lay some pipes so that YM can have water in another room now that the bath has been taken away.

Ever your affectionate, Florrie.

Clapham
February

Dear Old Mistress,

The Electrical Man has entered our lives. For some while now YM has been anxious to start painting the walls which have been put back - but apparently it is necessary for the electric wires to be in place before such decoration is done, or it will have to be disturbed again. The same principle affects the flooring - no boards to be nailed down until these magic wires are put underneath. Until now we have done perfectly well with flexes looped around the rooms, but it has been decreed that they are to be tidied away and any joins are to be made proper.

... no boards to be nailed down
until these magic wires are underneath

I like the Electrical Man; he is tall and thin and always ready to sit down and provide a lap for me. He generally arrives at the end of the afternoon and starts by turning off all the lights. A short spell of scrabbling about in the gathering dusk is soon followed by a break for tea and chat. This lasts until YM informs him she must have power back on in order to cook the supper, which he usually stays to share. After the meal more chatting - another couple of hours perhaps - before he departs. This pattern has been followed for some weeks, most of the wires still hang along the walls and YM is getting restive.

The weather is rather cold at present and I note that although there are radiators, they never become hot, or even slightly warm. We are awaiting four new window frames - the Man I Love has taken out the old ones and the plastic tacked up in the openings lets through some chilly draughts. How lucky my coat has thickened almost to its Litton density. When building operations stop for the day, we light a fire in the currently habitable room - this changes from time to time but fortunately most rooms have a fireplace - and fuel is provided by the fruits of the pulling down period. We have a good stock of old doors, windows, floors and scraped off wallpaper, so keep quite snug.

Affectionately, Florrie.

Clapham,
April

Dear Old Mistress,

I enjoyed a break in the country with you during the short absence of YM and the Man I Love. They went to France in order to buy a sink, so possibly we shall soon have a kitchen. The cooker has come down to the lower room and there has been a lot discussion and measurement going on about cupboards. Progress is visible in many directions - YM has been out cooking less and has begun to paint some of the upper rooms. She has bought a book on dragging, rolling and sponging; she reads bits out to us from time to time, but mostly she's going for plain stuff with a brush. It is more interesting when she and I go out in her car to collect building supplies; driving with YM in London is exciting - she knows lots of short cuts and I can often distract a rival vehicle at traffic lights by a well timed bark, so allowing us to shoot off in front.

A great new bath arrived, and with considerable effort was carried up to the highest room. The Man I Love has been occupied attaching pipes to it, but so far no water runs from them. He is evidently much pleased with this bath; I notice him stand back and gaze at it - just as I might, should a fresh shin

A great new bath

bone be laid before me and I was deciding where to make my first chew.

We have a new Electrical Man. This one is less sociable but the wires are being joined to switches and vanishing under the floors at a rapid rate. It will be rather dull when I can no longer get to the interesting spaces beneath the boards.

The Tall Fair Man and his Tired Girlfriend have left this house for one of their own, and there is talk of the Thick Dark Man going off to Foreign Parts. More disturbing to me are the plans for my YM and the Man I Love to undertake a Long Journey, and I hear no mention of my accompanying them.

Ever your affectionate, Florrie.

Clapham
May

Dear Old Mistress,

We have had a spell of sufficiently warm weather to make the final shedding of my winter coat occur, helped on its way by sudden heat in the radiators. YM is of the opinion that the present temperature needs no supplementing, and is impatient of the time spent by the Man I Love on small leaks of water in places and the strange noises of air in the pipes. She feels that priority should be given to causing water to run into the great bath. The special taps required for this have not yet arrived. and the Man I Love is not willing to compromise with any inferior models, even in the short term. He regards this bath as a work of art rather than a vehicle for washing.

The long awaited skip has come and gone. This was a large iron box dumped outside the house; as soon as it was in place everyone then present rushed to fill it with the various piles of debris collected over the past months which were not suitable to burn on the fire. I understand speed was necessary in case others in the street were tempted to make use of this receptacle. The rooms appeared rather empty after this operation - until now there has not been much room for furniture. I spent some time mopping up an assortment of insects left homeless by the removal of their shelter. YM insisted that the Man I Love, with my help, should make certain no spiders remained at large - she is funny about spiders.

A housewarming party for numerous relatives is planned for next month. I suspect YM felt the need of an incentive towards completion of the kitchen. She now has water at the sink, and the cooker works, but there are no cupboards, and she is loath to tile the floor or paint the walls before their installation. Ultimatums such as 'I cannot cook for 10/20/30 of your family/aunts/cousins with only a plank balanced on two oil cans for working surface' have been uttered. I await developments with interest.

Ever your affectionate, Florrie.

Summer, my fifth year

The lunch party took place. Amazing improvements had happened quite quickly. The cupboards came - no doors, but at least all YM's cooking paraphernalia could be put on the shelves, and they had tops so the cans and plank went to join the new and rapidly growing heap awaiting the next skip. YM painted the walls a deep yellow - the favourite colour of the Man I Love - and she laid the floor tiles quite neatly. They were warmer and less dusty than the concrete, but I found them a bit slippery if, having sensed an alien presence in the garden, I wanted to make a quick dash from my bed.

The lunch party took place

Upstairs we now had carpet - a nice shade of blue, becoming to me, and giving excellent purchase to my flying feet. I do wish humans would give more consideration to putting dog-friendly covering on kitchen floors. It is very rare to come across a surface on which a dog in a hurry can make progress without feeling the sensation of going backwards rather than forwards, of scrabbling and skidding rather than running smoothly, and of being generally insecure. It seems that an obsession with being able to wash the floor is responsible for this unpleasant shiny finish. Dog owners please note - a dog with a good lick can remove spillings of gravy, fat or milk expertly from carpet, though I suppose black coffee might have less appeal.

I digress; the luncheon cooked by my YM was of course delicious. By borrowing and by retrieving some useful pieces off the rubbish pile, seating was arranged for about thirty mixed relations, all of whom made many admiring comments about the transformation that had been performed on the house. I received these guests graciously - one of YM's final preparations had been to bath me and my bedcover - I felt lighter of some pounds of brick and cement dust, and looked my best. My appearance was a little marred when, holding me rather loosely under his arm while saying good-bye to an aunt, the Man I Love allowed me to fall into a puddle of rainwater at the kerbside - fortunately this was right at the end of the party.

This enjoyable event over, preparations for global travel became the main occupation. I understood that several oceans and continents were to be crossed, but few belongings could be taken because they all had to fit into something called a backpack. I was to be left with OM; I should be comfortable enough but would lack the challenges and trials I had encountered while the sole support of my Young Mistress. I accompanied the voyagers to the airport, received a last pat and hug and watched them disappear from my sight through a large gap in the wall.

Chalk Hill
September

Dear Young Mistress,

I was interested to receive your parcel for me - a strange little object. Its appearance reminded me of those tasteless buns you occasionally purchased in our London days, containing a barely edible round of compressed mince. I smelt it carefully - a flavour of rubber - and made a testing bite. I was much surprised when the thing emitted a curious mouse like squeak! The other dogs rushed up, thoroughly over-excited by the noise; I took it into my bed and allowed no one near me. OM said 'typically American' and added that she was surprised Customs had let it through. However it was a kind thought and has given the younger dogs some amusement.

... which tore at great speed around hairpin bends

What a lot of rushing about you are doing - skyscrapers, freeways, drive-ins, yankees - I was not able to completely follow your first letter, some words being unfamiliar to me. Now I believe you are among numerous islands with more odd names - Marie Gallant, Guadeloupe, Martinique, Dominica, St. Lucia, St. Vincent, Union, Granada and several others. There seems to have been a great deal of rain; OM says it would have been a warmer sort than that we experienced at Litton. Even so, you have had some alarming journeys between all these islands - planes unable to land, boats unable to set off, bridges washed away, and your description of taking a lift in the back of a local delivery truck which tore at great

67

speed around hairpin bends winding along the edge of a precipice made OM quite pale. I thought it sounded just the same as many of our trips across Exmoor, but perhaps more alarming for you as you were not on this occasion the driver.

We have heard much about Hurricane Henry causing devastation in your present part of the world. OM, and indeed the Master, were relieved when your letter - delayed by our postal strike - finally arrived telling us that you were now on the mainland of Venezuela, having travelled there by boat through particularly heavy rainstorms. They thought it strange that you did not appear to have heard of the hurricane.

Ever your affectionate, Florrie.

Chalk Hill
October

Dear Young Mistress,

Your travels become ever more dramatic! More torrential rain in Venezuela, when landslides of mud hold up the bus in which you ride and then you tell us you have crossed a river called the Orinoco which was three quarters of a mile wide. I find the company here excessive at times - your young brother recently described me as an only dog and on the whole I prefer to be so - but your latest news does not make me hanker to leave my place by the Aga and join you. Long hours in a bus, three days to climb a mountain with a flat top* - can this be right? - and the food you describe as a mix of rice, spaghetti, manioc powder, potato, and occasional very tough meat, does not appeal. El Dorado - gold mines and prisons, the Brazilian border and more long bus journeys before you reached Manaus, a brief stay followed by days and days in different boats floating down the Amazon until at Belem you took to yet more buses. Your story of the madman on the boat who stole the jersey of the Man I Love, and

* Mt. Roraima, Venezuela

... a mountain with a flat top

attempted to unwrap you from your hammock throughout the night before being overpowered and placed under restraint caused us much concern. You are in wild places - having already had your camera stolen, and now you tell us that the Man I Love's watch has been stripped from his wrist in the main street of Belem in daytime!

I am sorry to learn that some of that unpleasant food has disagreed with you and that you have an upset stomach. I recommend a good meal of grass first thing in the morning. OM says she will be very glad to hear that you have reached the farm in the south of Brazil where your older brother works and to know that you are in safe hands for a while at least.

We spent a weekend on Exmoor and had a good walk up on the common near Litton. As we turned homewards a familiar and strong smell struck my nose; I followed it up and what should emerge from a clump of gorse but the unmistakable shape of the most persistent of the Litton foxes! I gave chase at my best possible speed and Hera joined me, but that cheeky creature merely trotted away towards the road. We were gaining fast but were sadly checked by agonised screams from OM who feared we would be too carried away to take proper notice of any motor traffic that might be passing. Such a pity.

Affectionately, Florrie.

Chalk Hill
January

Dear Young Mistress,

I was pleased to catch the sound of your voice when the Christmas telephone calls were made, and I think OM was happy to know you were, if temporarily, staying in some comfort and security in your brother's household. I overheard her questioning the logic of you leaving there after your first short visit to travel a great distance to a place by the name of Tierra del Fuego, and returning by way of all sorts of hazards to join the holiday festivities. Perhaps the heat of Brazil was oppressive - certainly the glaciers, icebergs, snow and wind you encountered further south were more akin to Litton. I would have found a bird that cannot fly most frustrating, what strange creatures those penguins must be. Your walks in the Parque Paine sounded strenuous also exceedingly cold and damp, though the livestock interesting - I could have cleared off the geese for you, but I don't think I would have fancied the idea of wading through the deep cold rivers. How did you get dry again - one does need some good dry bedding to roll around on - was that to be found in the tin huts where you spent the nights?

The tale of the drunken lift you took on your way from the Parque to the coast caused OM to shudder and say she was often very glad that she heard about your adventures only when they were over. You must have been relieved to return to land after four days in a cargo boat voyaging up the sea beside Chile in constant mist and rain and have felt ready to go back to dryer and warmer conditions.

By comparison we have had a quiet time here, mild weather and plenty of pheasants to keep off the ground. Nell and Daisy are quite sharp at this game; I recognise Daisy has the family nose which obviates the need to rush about like Nell - we can both cover the ground quite fast when really necessary. Nell is always haring about in front, while we take the trouble to sniff over every little message left by those creatures that have passed before us. Sometimes this makes OM quite impatient - I can't think why.

Ever your affectionate, Florrie.

... in the Parque Paine

Chalk Hill
March

Dear Young Mistress,

How remarkable that there should be a town in those faraway places bearing my name - Florianapolis! Quite an agreeable place too by your report. But now you are far from the seaside and among the mountains of the Andes in the wild lands of Bolivia and Peru. OM seems particularly concerned for your safety in the latter - we gather you plan a trek along an Inca trail and there are apprehensions that your tent may be slashed open and your goods

71

seized. This is obviously an occasion when you need a good dog to guard you - one of the larger varieties, possibly an Alsatian or Dobermann - could one be hired? A Cavalier would be out of place in such a situation - our jaws were not developed to seize a bandito by the leg.

... a rather low sort of terrier

Life here runs smoothly. I was momentarily concerned the other weekend when your young brother turned up with a rather low sort of terrier - you could cut the Cockney accent with a knife! My initial worry that OM would add yet another dog to the household was eased when I heard her commend the specimen as a 'knowing little thing' but add very firmly that she was not prepared to take her on. It appears that the unfortunate - or perhaps fortunate - creature was dumped on your young brother's doorstep by the refuse collectors who had found her wandering the streets. She is of indeterminate years, certainly past middle-age, and having observed her resolute attachment to your brother, I do not think he will have much chance of avoiding ownership. Why she left her previous home remains a mystery - she is stout in build and shows evidence of being an experienced thief. I daresay she will make him an adequate companion and be of some use as a guard once she learns to be selective - we heard she had already bitten two callers to his flat, and one was a customer.

Very affectionately, Florrie.

Chalk Hill
April

Dear Young Mistress,

OM said your reversed charge call from Cuzco was well worth the cost - around £60 - to know the latest stage of your journeying was safely accomplished. We have received some parcels containing various items you have purchased and understandably do not want to carry across the South Pacific. Most of them are intact; the painted glass frames around the mirrors are cracked in places, but OM thinks she can get them mended; the rolled-up oil paintings are fine and the majority of the numerous little objects that were wrapped in your no-longer-wanted cold weather clothing are whole. I have sniffed over everything carefully, and whilst I can detect some familiar personal odours, they are overlaid with a mix of other smells - coffee, cigarillos, burnt meat, as well as some with which I am unfamiliar but that are perhaps peculiar to South America. Some of the clothes are a little mouldy too.

OM and the Master have been studying the globe; they point to the middle of a large blue expanse, find one or two small dots and then have difficulty in reading the names. I believe they are trying to plot the route you are taking on your way to Australia. I understand you are taking to the air rather than boats for most of the way. Very wise - there does look a lot of sea. OM has spent a long time looking through her telephone directory and has announced that it will not be possible to make connection with most of the islands that you plan to visit; they are apparently not mentioned under international calls.

We are hoping you have heard that there is a new member of the family - your older brother's wife has a baby daughter. I know something about small humans and have learnt to be polite while keeping my distance, though I daresay such a very young one will not yet attempt to pull my tail.

Ever your affectionate, Florrie.

Chalk Hill
May

Dear Young Mistress,

Your letter written in part from Easter Island and also from the Tuamotos group has come. I note you prefer the South Pacific diet to the South American but personally am not sure that coconuts and tropical fruits hold much appeal. The fish would be all right, provided the bones had been removed. All that swimming in the sea peering at fish, even colourful fish, cannot be good for one's coat, and I suspect your hair may have changed colour yet again before you return to these shores. OM says this letter will be sent to straight to Australia, she has little confidence that you and the Man I Love will stick to the itinerary last proposed and feels there is no point in our joint literary efforts languishing in the Post Office of some unvisited tropical isle.

We look forward to your eventual homecoming later this summer. It will coincide with the annual leave of your brother, his wife and their baby; also three of your Argentine cousins plan a trip to the Old World at the same time. OM is planning a celebration party of some magnitude - tents are booked, flowers, music and food is arranged - it all sounds similar to the wedding of your brother and I remember on that day, *when* I was finally released from the stable, there were excellent pickings, so I shall look forward to the festivities. I shall hope to come to the airport to welcome you; as long as OM is prepared to maintain that I am a travelling dog - and she is not usually fussy about such little fictions - there is no problem about my admittance.

It is thought our contact with you will be more predictable when you finally reach Australia.

Ever your affectionate, Florrie.

... from Easter Island

Summer, my sixth year

My young mistress - and the Man I Love - returned more or less as planned. They looked a bit thinner but otherwise well. The new baby, now three months old, also arrived with her parents. I was glad to find that my assessment about the lack of hazard from such a young child was correct, and that I was able to stroll quite close to her as she lay on her sheepskin mat, waving my tail to signify polite approval, without the least danger of it being seized. Nell and Daisy were initially much alarmed by the smallness of the person and the strange noises she made, and for some days only entered the same room reluctantly. My confident and relaxed approach gradually influenced them, but they remained cautious throughout her stay. The Argentine cousins, a delightful family with a proper respect for a Royal dog, arrived, and the great party was held.

I do particularly enjoy a social occasion ...

I would have liked more opportunity to assist in the preparations; I know better than to get in the way of lorries delivering marquees, neither do I thieve food, even when left at provocatively low level, but OM must have felt that my companions were not so high-minded and we were too frequently shut away. At least once the party was under way I was, at the special insistence of my young mistress, allowed to mingle, and as usual I received much admiration and was

76

passed several tasty little snacks. I do particularly enjoy a social occasion, my natural savoir faire comes to the fore and I am certain that, as I stand at the front door, tail waving a gracious welcome, I add immense tone to any gathering.

Shortly after these happenings, my Young Mistress and the Man I Love returned from a day's excursion, and announced they were to be married. There was great excitement and pleasure all round, though later I did hear OM say to the Master why ever had they just given a large party when they would now have to do it all over again next spring. Even so, I think they are pleased.

I accompanied my young mistress on some of the visits she made to London, but it was a hot summer and quite often I had to remain in some unfamiliar and stuffy flat while she was out, so I tactfully made it clear that I was prepared to stay at our country home during her short absences. She and the Man I Love planned to return to Australia, where they had bought a house. I came to understand it was not practical for me to take up Australian citizenship - should I have done so I would have had to spend several months in some public kennels, and after passing through this time of quarantine, would have been no longer permitted to return to the land of my birth. I resigned myself to a life in the company of Nell, Daisy and Hera; I do not find it difficult to distance myself when I feel the need for solitude, OM and the Master quite appreciate that I am a unique dog - and the food is good.

Once more I visited Heathrow to wave a paw to my young mistress. She was to return early next year to assist with the wedding plans. Young pheasants were becoming too tame for my peace of mind, much in need of putting to exercise in the air, and I settled down to the autumn routine.

Chalk Hill
September

Dear Young Mistress,

Such a shock - *there are puppies!* I had thought Nell was getting rather portly but I did not suspect this happening. There are three in number, all males, and their mother seems obsessed with them and the need to keep them constantly clean - probably just as well. Their box has, rather to my annoyance, been placed in the prime position before the Aga. I limit myself to one or two glances over the edge during the day and I then give a polite wave of my tail to indicate approval. One must show good manners even when somewhat concerned at the effect this increase in population may have on one's future comfort.

... there are puppies!

Others in the household are less restrained - Daisy is apparently mesmerised and joins Nell in the wash routine whenever permitted. She does not appear to have the natural expertise of the mother, her licking being carried out in a dabbing and darting manner but Nell is remarkably tolerant and only occasionally rejects this rather clumsy assistance. I can assure you that I feel no wish to join the party! They are growing very rapidly, inevitable I suppose as they feed ceaselessly, and are beginning to move around their bed. How long, I ask myself, will they remain blessedly confined? And what will happen when - horrible thought - they roam free?

I was interested to hear conditions in your new house are so similar to those that prevailed in the London home of the Man I Love. From time to time I hear OM express her amazement as to how you stand it - but I could tell her much of the advantages of living in a half destroyed house. If there are no floorboards, many interesting objects and smells are exposed among the foundations; if there are no windows, leaving the house in a hurry is simple and one can put the neighbour's cat to flight without delay. Water and washing is something one can well do without. OM took it into her head to bath us all the other day - she thought we had brought fleas back from Exmoor - and it is a most unpleasant experience. Being well dried afterwards is the only bearable part of the operation.

Ever your affectionate, Florrie.

Chalk Hill
January

Dear Young Mistress,

Another year is here, and we look forward to your return next month. We spent Christmas at the Exmoor house, being joined by your maternal Grandmother and her two dachshunds. The younger one made brave efforts to follow us over the moor, but it is an unsuitable terrain for a dog with such short legs. She would attempt to take a direct route and then had to proceed by a series of high jumps over the heather which did not carry her forward any great distance. Constant high pitched yaps - although at times helpful in locating her whereabouts - did nothing to assist her progress.

I am very relieved to report that those puppies departed last month. My worst fears were realised when it became no longer practical to keep them enclosed, even in the hen run brought into the kitchen for the purpose. Before this stage and while they were learning to eat like proper dogs, there were some spin-offs. The left-overs of tasty little meals of chicken or minced beef were sometimes added to my dish, but gradually OM instigated periods of release and free play - peaceful life was over. The little thugs, having already shredded their mother's ears and tail - not that her tail was ever much to write home about - made advances upon my handsome plume! I made it extremely clear that this *would not do,* but unabashed the wretches invaded my bed; here I found it more difficult to dislodge them for by this time they were at least half my size. If they remained still, it was not too bad - at this time of year some extra warmth is welcome, but stillness was not natural to them. When I could, I nipped through to take my ease on the sofa or armchair, but this was not often possible - thanks to the incontinence of the little brutes, the door giving access to my comfortable retreat was generally kept shut.

OM is glad to hear progress is being made with your house, and that some of your visitors have departed. It must have been difficult to keep them all fed in the midst of the building works, especially when the kitchen was the centre of these operations.

Affectionately, Florrie.

... the wretches invaded my bed

Spring, my seventh year

Young Mistress duly returned to help with the preparations for the wedding. She and OM spent a lot of time consulting lists, but there was plenty of attention for me and we made some pleasant little trips together visiting relations - just the two of us, which is what I like best. Nearer the Day, the Man I Love came back; unfortunately he had visited some other foreign land en route and had caught a fever. He suffered much and I took the opportunity to administer comfort by lying on the end of his bed. With this assistance he recovered in time for the Wedding Day.

I was fully involved in the immediate preparations - supervision of marquee pitching, checking out caterer's supplies, accompanying young sister and her friend while they arranged flowers in all directions - but once more we found ourselves shut in a stable for the main part of the festivities. However, I was eventually rescued and took some part in the Going Away, being decorated with a large yellow ribbon and carried out by the Man I Love. There were a lot of exceedingly loud bangs and flashes in the sky - the Master does like his fireworks - and

... took some part in the Going Away

finally Young Mistress and the Man I Love drove away in a car curiously hung about with various objects. Later we had a very good time crumbing in the marquee and found many tasty remnants.

The newly-weds did not reappear for some weeks - on their travels again I came to understand - and the only news of their whereabouts was a postcard smelling of garlic. I overheard OM say tersely that it was understandable to hear nothing when they were in the middle of the Pacific but that she could do with knowing whether they were alive or dead while in Europe, and when were they going to deal with all their presents filling up the house. One day in early summer they returned, and it was very good to have them back. I gave the Man I Love a special welcome - he calls me Bonzo and holds me in a rather insecure way under his arm; he has even dropped me once and I fell in a puddle - but even so there is something about him that I find *irresistible*. They soon went off to London, and as there were no exciting building operations going on in which I could take part, I remained mostly in the country.

I spent cosy hours ... in her old room

Young Mistress came to see me frequently and I spent cosy hours on the sheepskin rug in her old room while she fiddled about sorting out various belongings. Their intention was to go back to their house in Australia; YM had to decide what was to be packed up and sent out in something called a container. They seemed in no great hurry to leave, but finally autumn came and their day of departure arrived. I did not go to the airport on this occasion - on my previous visit we had observed a number of large notices concerning dogs, and OM thought it wiser for me to make my farewells previously. Also, there was a lot of luggage and hardly room in the car for even a small dog. I heard OM make a number of stipulations about immediate notification of safe arrival, and when she returned home she was very glad to sit with me on her lap for a while - such partings are indeed painful but we give each other comfort and consolation.

Chalk Hill
October

Dear Young Mistress,

We were glad to hear from you and to have some photographs of your house. OM says there looks plenty to do yet but she supposes you are used to living like that. I think she liked the plan of your garden best, she seemed impressed you have managed to clear enough rubble away to find some earth. I would be pleased to come and help catch the spiders you tell us are abundant, but OM says poisonous types frequent that part of the world so perhaps it's as well I cannot be there. We hope your furniture will turn up soon - OM has checked that it has left these shores and the shippers expect it will be with you by Christmas.

We have settled into a familiar routine here. As I have mentioned before, three on a lap is impossible and two a crowd. When we are not overrun with visitors, laps after dinner in the dining room can be allocated quite conveniently. Daisy is most happy to stretch out before the electric fire; she has always been a heat lover and more so since her accident, and she will bake contentedly until the smell of singeing hair causes OM to move her slightly further away. The Master lights up a cigar at the end of the meal, but before doing so he will often pass me a small piece of cheese. This has to be done secretly as OM does not approve and say it leads to begging and 'making a nuisance of oneself at meals'. I'm afraid Nell *is* a little tactless in her attentions to the Master when the cheese is on the table.

Once the cigar is lit I leave the Master well alone - this is not a smell I care for, but I have to tell you that Nell is positively *addicted* and can't wait to jump up, place her chin on the Master's elbow, close her eyes and breath in the fumes! This means OM's lap is free for me, and until she gets up to clear off, we have a comfortable time. Even so, there can be problems here, because OM is working on a tapestry which she has put on a frame. I have tried remaining curled up and still under this work, but from time to time I am struck on the head by the corner of the frame - it is a large one - and this is not desirable. Luckily the days are getting shorter, OM needs a special light to see to sew and she seldom remembers to bring it in beforehand. If I can establish myself with the coffee, I am generally undisturbed.

Affectionately, Florrie.

Chalk Hill
November

Dear Young Mistress,

Winter approaches; the leaves are falling and the evenings getting darker. A couple of very irritating pheasants have taken to roosting in the big apple tree. They make a great fuss and to-do about arranging themselves for the night - so annoying, one can hear them flapping around in a very heavy way up in the branches, but however hard I and Daisy bark, we cannot get them airborne. Just when I think I've succeeded in unsettling them, OM comes out and tells us to stop that row.

I am prepared to acknowledge some sense of kinship with Daisy - we both have *subtlety*, a quality completely lacking in Nell, a warm hearted and affectionate dog, but quite without guile. Daisy can also display extra sensory perception, and I was glad of this recently. I had gone into the shed at the bottom of the back yard where the apples are stored, also the paper for burning collected - and this sometimes includes promising smelly little parcels. OM is inclined to discourage me from following her when she goes into this shed, so I creep in quietly behind her. The problem of such unseen entry is that I am not always observed and called out when the door is closed again, and thus I sometimes find myself shut in for longer than I would wish.

Naturally a Cavalier does not do anything vulgar like barking or whining to draw attention to oneself, particularly when one has entered a shed privately. If I am shut out of the main house, and the fault is that of the humans, I have no hesitation of giving several good thumps against the back door and this usually ensures instant admission. On the occasion I mention, I had spent at least half an hour in the apple shed, and having exhausted the possibilities of mice under the racks, greasy or meaty paper around the

... a persistent shrill barking

burning bin and so on, was quite pleased to hear young Daisy start up a persistent shrill barking outside the closed door. Her bark carries, and soon OM came to investigate. She had not missed me - there are *too many* of us at present what with the dachshunds and that terrier staying - and was surprised to see me stroll out when she opened the door. I was relieved to emerge - it was nearly tea time.

Ever your affectionate, Florrie.

Chalk Hill,
December

Dear Young Mistress,

So OM is shortly to visit you - I keep hearing her say 'I hope it will be *after* Christmas' and certainly we expect her to be here to cook a good turkey with all trimmings - I don't quite understand why there should be uncertainty.

We've just had a weekend on Exmoor. After some early snow a number of deer had found their way into the garden. Daisy and I tracked them carefully and discovered where they had jumped in. OM was not pleased with their hoof prints all over that large flower bed where she spends hours messing about, and there was much talk of deer fencing. I understand they can make enormous leaps. Of course if we were around for more of the time they would not be so daring. The rabbits in the bank are as plentiful as ever, but that annoying wire that keeps me from taking a walk whenever I feel like it over to the farm sheds seems to have kept them out of the garden, much to OM's relief. She becomes extraordinarily cross when she finds traces of their presence among her plants. There were some bare patches in the lawn, but it's thought these were caused by crows searching for worms. *They* wouldn't have been allowed to land in my presence.

OM says she is maintaining a nature reserve rather than a garden - she does not seem too enthusiastic about this, which is not consistent because she positively *encourages* some of the birds here by putting food out on a special table.

Ever your affectionate, Florrie.

Chalk Hill
January

Dear Young Mistress,

The Master and I are sending you this card with our love and congratulations on the arrival of your baby girl - it's a pretty horrid pink flowery card; I would have chosen something more interesting, but was not consulted. I understand the baby came within twenty four hours of OM's arrival - convenient timing - you can rely on her to keep the Man I Love fed properly while you are otherwise engaged with your young. From my observation they are demanding little things.

Love and licks, Florrie.

Chalk Hill
February

Dear Young Mistress,

We are pleased to have OM back with first hand news of you and the offspring. I believe she is a very good feeder with little regard for whether it is day or night. This no doubt can be tiring, but the advantage of her being - for the present anyway - restricted to her basket, is considerable. I shudder when I recall those rampant destructive puppies - at least you only have one.

We have had a good time with the Master in charge. He fully realises my privileged status and we made several small excursions on our own. I know my way round his Department at the hospital well and am made most welcome there. We also called upon your paternal Grandmother in Gloucestershire; she is always gracious to me - though I take a dismissive line with her overfed and somewhat fierce terrier.

I observe that Nell is putting on some weight and I quite expected OM would reduce her diet - she usually takes a critical look at our figures when she has been away - but rather to my surprise I notice that such delicacies as the cheese rinds, the gravy from the roast, even an occasional egg, are going Nell's way. I don't grudge her the major share of the green vegetables for I only eat my Brussels sprout under protest; indeed it has to be well chopped and mixed in for me to contemplate it at all - but can it be right that she should have *all* the best left-overs?

Ever your affectionate, Florrie.

Nell is putting on some weight ...

Chalk Hill
March

Dear Young Mistress,

Is all this reproduction catching? What I dreaded has come to pass: *there are more puppies.* I did wonder if this blow was about to fall - as I observed to you in earlier correspondence positive selection was being practised in favour of Nell when the meals were being prepared, and of course I am, after the previous episode, more experienced in interpreting such signs. There are four *and three are female*, which makes me extremely apprehensive that the canine population here may be increased permanently. I notice that names have been allocated, and whereas the previous batch were simply referred to as Pig, Black Pig and Little Pig, such appellations as Blondie and Phoebe have a more long term ring. I am seriously worried.

However I conceal all this from the proud mother as I wander past their box - in which they are mercifully still contained, being as yet only at the squirming-about-on-the-stomach stage, and wave my tail in benign approval. Daisy is as besotted as before and her help with the cleaning up a little more relaxed. She wisely leaves the really grubby stuff to the fond parent.

Daisy is as besotted as before ...

My tranquillity is also disturbed by the coming back from foreign parts of your brother and his family. Their youngster is now fully mobile, but proceeds in a totally unpredictable manner. This can be most disconcerting - she is liable to join me on the dog bed without warning, and when she speeds round the kitchen, shouting merrily and pulling a row of squeaking wooden ducks behind her, I find it best to take refuge in some quiet corner. I had been told by small child experienced acquaintances that excellent pickings would positively rain upon one from the high chair during feeding time, no such luck - the little glutton scoffs everything she is given. I believe their residence here is only temporary and my hope is that their house hunting will soon be successful; there is at present too much emphasis placed on the needs of the younger generation.

I look forward to your visit next month very much, and as long as your baby is not yet moving about, will be glad to see her too. I have come to the conclusion that I can only tolerate these juveniles when they are static; having constantly to find new hiding places is most wearing.

Ever your affectionate, Florrie.

... pulling a row of squeaking wooden ducks behind her

Spring, my eighth year

My Young Mistress and her offspring duly returned for a month's stay, and I was relieved to find her baby mostly comatose and although she screamed a bit in the evenings, OM generally went upstairs and dealt with *that* while I reposed, unchallenged, on my Young Mistress's lap. This was very pleasant and I felt, for the time being at least, top dog once more. Those puppies were confined to a wire run in a corner; one or two likely new owners came to see them, holding them up and cooing over them in a perfectly nauseous manner, and it seemed to me that all I had feared - the overcrowding on the beds by exuberant and obstreperous youngsters, competition for bones, general lack of respect, diverting of attention from Me, might not happen.

The christening of the new baby took place, followed by a large lunch party and on this occasion I almost wished I had been placed in the stable - for my own safety. Numerous small children hurtled about the house - parental control appeared non-existent - and although food was dropped freely, one ran considerable risk of being run down or over during retrieval. Eventually all were marshalled together and a walk took place - I joined a convoy of prams and pushchairs and we set off down the lane where out in the open I found it simpler to avoid the pounding feet, and had a good time sniffing over the traces of other weekend walkers and their dogs. Generally OM takes us round the fields, thus frustrating what she calls my 'suburbanising down the drive'.

My Young Mistress's stay passed quickly. Soon after her departure OM declared it was no longer possible to keep the puppies enclosed and the horrid business of them being free began. I put them very sharply in their place when I found my bedspace being invaded, and otherwise waited in hope for the new owners to return and claim their chosen one. This did indeed happen on two occasions and away went the dog pup and one of the females to homes previously judged suitably doting by OM.

Two still remained .....

... the horrid business of them being free began

EVER YOUR AFFECTIONATE

(This letter accompanies a card showing several Blenheim coloured Cavaliers playing together)

Chalk Hill
July

Dear Young Mistress,

Please do not think because I have placed my mark upon this card that I can do more than barely tolerate the young brats - though occasionally they have their uses such as providing a little extra warmth and comfort in the bed. Phoebe - Feeble I would rather say - is a dog of very few brains and a rather weak bladder, and shows signs of developing speed more suited to a greyhound than a stately Cavalier. She has a disagreeable way of showing indiscriminate affection first thing in the morning, very jarring at such an hour. I have a little more hope for the other one, though she is poorly marked, far too much white, and why draw attention to this lamentable flaw by calling her Blondie? However she is beginning to show a serious interest in moth and insect hunting. and can display a little more restraint in her emotions than her sister, particularly towards her elders and betters.

... the young brats

Yesterday a large number of people were expected to lunch and the kitchen became a trifle noisy; I therefore took myself up to the attic bedroom to meditate in peace and quiet. Shortly before the arrival of the guests, I was missed and cries of 'Florrie' were heard resounding through the house and gardens. It was rather gratifying to realise all members of the household had engaged themselves in the search - sometimes I wonder if, as one of a *pack,* my absence would be remarked at all. The attic door had blown nearly shut - of course I could have extracted myself if I had chosen to do so - and eventually your young sister, coming up on some other errand, discovered my whereabouts. Your young brother was recalled from the direction of the village, the Master was summoned back from the woods and preparations for the lunch resumed.

I hope you have a good time on your birthday, and that your baby is being decently disciplined and kept to the corner of the bed.

Ever your affectionate, Florrie.

Chalk Hill
September

Dear Young Mistress,

I was pleased to have news of you and your youngster, and of course of the Man I Love, from your faraway home when the Master returned after visiting you. Here we go along in a somewhat humdrum way - I look back to the challenges of my youth at Litton and London with nostalgic feelings, but in general I am content with my place here. I cannot say I like the tendency of both OM and the Master to refer to me as 'the old dog', although I am sure this refers to my wisdom and seniority rather than to any state of decrepitude. I am still the preferred companion of the Master for solitary outings when appropriate.

I had an unpleasant experience at the vet's recently. OM took me to surgery because my ears had been irritating and causing me to scratch them a lot. On hearing this, the officious young man there peered down them and also had a close look at my jaws and teeth. He then announced that several of my teeth were in a bad state and must come out! An appointment was made and OM duly delivered me up. I recall waiting some time in a small cage floored with newspaper - not the type of surroundings where one feels at home. I was later taken from this place by a girl in a white coat, then comes a blank in my memory. My next recollection is being back there and feeling extremely shaky and unbalanced. I think I slept a little and on waking was placed on my lead. Calling upon all a Cavalier's reserves of dignity and deportment in the face of adversity, I managed to follow the girl in a more or less steady manner and was most relieved to find OM waiting to take me home. She had brought a blanket and hot water bottle, but I preferred her lap and although she does not usually permit this when she is driving, I was allowed to remain.

Once home, every attention was paid to me - my favourite bean bag placed before the fire, puppies repelled from joining me and a tasty light supper served. After a good night's rest - beside OM's bed, I felt quite myself, and I have to admit that I am now able to tackle a bone without discomfort, while my ears have given no further trouble.

We have recently endured the company of your young brother's terrier for some time. I don't mind meeting her on a day visit; we quite enjoy exchanging some London news, but a week is a bit much. She is so constantly restless and her manners are not what we are used to. I hesitate to tell you that I actually observed her jump on top of the dishwasher and leave the kitchen by way of the window! Another time I caught her scrabbling through the wire and hedge barrier near the garages - such a poor example for those young puppies - in an attempt to join OM in the vegetable garden. I can't believe OM felt the need for her company while she picked beans; she would have taken me had she wanted canine support.

Those youngsters continue to grow, hulking uncouth creatures that they are. I try to demonstrate the art of dignified reticence, but I think my example totally passes them by. That Phoebe will positively *swarm* all over one - a sort of uncontrolled chumminess I find very hard to bear. They really should be made to realise that they should *not* appropriate the best place on the sofa in the evening. The only benefit of their existence that I can call to mind is that OM now purchases some rather good thick chews which I quite fancy myself. OM is not entirely sympathetic to this; she has a tendency to take them away and redistribute to those undeserving louts - but I manage by careful watching to nip one up for myself pretty often.

Ever your affectionate, Florrie.

... to nip one up for myself pretty often

Chalk Hill
January

Dear Young Mistress,

Are you sure you are not being a little over-enthusiastic in adopting some of the curious habits prevalent in your new land? I have heard of the strange animals in that country who instead of sensibly leaving their young at base when they need to exercise or feed, take them along in a sort of attached pocket - and now you undertake a five day walk along the rocky coast of Tasmania with the Very Young Mistress strapped to your back. I believe the Man I Love was burdened with the food, bedding and shelter necessary for you all, and it does not appear that conditions for this latest trek were ideal. You write that it is wholly satisfying to sit around a camp fire at

... a walk around the rocky coast of Tasmania

the end of the day with the billy on the boil (I do not follow this exactly - however the gist is clear), but to gain this satisfaction is it really necessary to first struggle through mud, swamps and rain forest; tackle steep climbs - both up and down; wade through icy creeks or cross them by insecure bridges - and all the while no communication possible except by sending up a flare, or passing messages by another chance-met walker. OM and the Master were concerned by this last aspect, but made their usual comment - 'she has always made everything as difficult for herself as possible'. They do not seem surprised by your choice of holiday, just relieved to hear it has now been safely accomplished. I expect the blisters on the soles of your feet will soon heal.

I myself still much enjoy a walk on the moor, but the circumstances have to be right; I do not care for such an outing in the early part of the morning, when I am digesting my breakfast, and it is certainly inappropriate to expect one of my years to ascend the steep side of the common in the teeth of a hailstorm. I had to make this quite clear last weekend - I simply sat down and looked pointedly over my shoulder to where the car was parked by the roadside. Those young dogs had already disappeared over the horizon, so OM had little choice; she carried me, tucked inside her jacket until level ground was reached and a change of direction brought relief from the strong wind.

Ever your affectionate, Florrie.

Chalk Hill
Spring, my ninth year

Dear Young Mistress,

So you expect to increase your family again later this year. Is this really wise? Personally I find the clamour and demands of extreme youth - whether it be human or canine - most exhausting. From time to time your older brother's offspring - now two in number and both mobile - come to spend the day with OM. Although my technique of sinking down into my beanbag and feigning deep sleep is usually successful, and leaves Hera and the junior dogs to take the brunt of their attentions, total relaxation is not possible while small children are in the house.

Those adolescent Cavaliers, though full grown, show few signs of true maturity and cause me some unease. Phoebe, like her mother, is a simple and warm-hearted individual. I would prefer *not* to have my face washed after breakfast, but I am sure she means well and I am prepared occasionally to share my bed with her. That Blondie is another matter altogether - a sly fawning creature, in whom I detect ambition to be the spoilt favourite of OM. There is little about her to support this conceit: short in the jaw, thickset in build, poorly marked and of devious character. She has a creepy habit of hopping up to occupy the warm place left whenever one of our humans vacates a chair - even a dining room chair. Such behaviour would *never* have been allowed in my puppy days. OM is getting very lax. I admit the little beast shows considerable determination when forcing her square and solid body into bramble thickets to drive out some cowering pheasant, but should there be the least hint of another bird in the vicinity, she hurtles on, totally deaf to OM's most ringing cries. Often the only way to assess her whereabouts is to look around for the next bird to fly up - and the next - until she finally reappears, completely unrepentant. *Much* stricter discipline should be administered.

Affectionately, Florrie.

... even a
dining room chair

On Exmoor
Summer

Dear Young Mistress,

So the Master is visiting you again, and you have all journeyed to the northern parts of your country and are, in spite of the scorpions and spiders that abound in that region, much enjoying a camping holiday. OM is surprised - any suggestion she has ever put to the Master of sleeping in a tent while travelling has always been firmly rejected; even so he appears to find this new experience quite stimulating.

During his absence, we have been staying at the Exmoor home where interesting building works are under way. I feel myself to be something of an expert in such things, but have been disappointed by OM's unwillingness to let me inspect and assist. As yet it is unclear what will result from the scraping up of earth into heaps, and holes being made, then filled with cement, but it *is* clear that a feast can be had if I succeed in entering the garage unperceived. This is where the workmen take their meals, and they are marvellously casual at leaving around open packets of biscuits, cartons of milk and discarded sandwiches. For a time OM failed to realise that the garden was no longer dog proof - this has always annoyed me - and I had one or two fine feeds, but those wretched youngsters - so lacking in finesse - began to make an obvious beeline for the booty. We now take closely supervised runs, sometimes even being put on leads to prevent us crossing the latest earthwork created by the bulldozer. It has rained extremely hard most of the time since we came here. OM says she will not have the entire house turned into a building site until she has to.

We have had some good walks over the moor, and I have been quite glad to let the coming generation take on the task of keeping those twittering larks on the move. Annoying little birds, they dip down, skim one's nose and then hang about almost in reach until you think their tail feathers are within gulp, when away they go again. They are really best ignored, but if Phoebe chooses to dash off in hopeless pursuit both dog and bird are well exercised.

Ever your affectionate, Florrie.

... marvellously casual at leaving around open packets of biscuits

Autumn

OM went off in her turn to visit my Young Mistress, and soon we heard that there was another Very Small Mistress - OM reported she was a little less noisy than her sister. The Master and I duly despatched a paw marked pink card and made a couple of Exmoor trips together. It was becoming evident that the building activities would result in some extra rooms, and I was pleased to overhear that time and attention was being paid to the correct siting of the dog beds in the new kitchen. The Master was less fussy about preventing me from having a good run over the new works; it brought back nostalgic memories of my days as chief assistant to the Man I Love.

Chalk Hill
December

Dear Young Mistress

It is reassuring to have OM back in time for Christmas, we are well cared for in her absence but I am relieved to be certain that she will be in charge of the turkey. She becomes quite generous at distributing the remains once the main meal is consumed, and there is good broth added to our breakfasts well into the New Year.

As you know at weekends I often drop in at the Master's hospital office, but recently I made a most stimulating excursion to London in his company. I have noted, by the scents about his clothes, that he is making frequent journeys to the metropolis - the smell of London is unmistakable and my travels with you by train when I was bought - rather resentfully on your part - my own ticket, has enabled me to identify his usual mode of transport. However last week we set off by car, and the moment we stepped out onto the pavement I observed that we had come to a spacious and elegant part of the city. A short walk soon brought us to large glass doors covered with ironwork through which we were admitted following some strange clicking sounds.

Inside a lady seated behind a desk greeted us and after some pleasant exchanges we ascended to an upper floor by lift. This caused an odd sensation in my stomach which I recall feeling once before when accompanying you on an expedition to a large shop during our Clapham days. When later we descended a great number of stairs before coming to ground level, I felt the minor discomfort had been well worth while - I do get a trifle out of breath nowadays when proceeding uphill.

The President's dog!

I anticipate - we went into a room with thick carpet and a shiny sofa and chairs, and only the quantity of papers and books lying about made me realise that this was his place of work. While the Master fiddled about at the desk I made a careful inspection of this room but found nothing of interest, excepting a few crumbs of digestive biscuit under a chair. We descended to a lower floor and went into an area which I *could* recognise as an office - there were the usual sort of humming and tapping machines and a lady who gave me a kind welcome. The Master left me in her charge for a short time - once we were alone I received a piece of chocolate - and I sat politely beside her keeping the tip of my tail just moving a little to indicate I would be prepared to accept a further portion. Suddenly the door opened and a tall man strode in; he eyed me in a hostile way and asked 'What is *that* doing here?' 'This,' said my new friend 'is the President's dog!' What a ring that has! I stood up and gave him my most Royal and superior look - which he was quite unable to meet.

When the Master returned we left the building and took a stroll in the nearby Regent's Park - the Master told me the name. The title 'President's dog' rang in my head and I stepped out very grandly. Back at home that evening the other dogs greeted me with particular effusiveness, curious to know where I had been. I felt able to treat even the youngsters with tolerance, secure in the knowledge that, as President's dog, my superiority could never be questioned.

Ever your affectionate, Florrie.

Chalk Hill
January

Dear Young Mistress,

I am very pleased to hear that you *and* the Man I Love - and I must suppose the Small Mistresses - plan to return for a month's stay later this year. Is there any chance the younger one might be at the playpen stage? This does allow one to indulge in a post-prandial nap confident one will not be abruptly tweaked or sat upon. Walking out with pram or pushchair suits me admirably - the pace tends to be slower and allows plenty of time for me to linger at the clumps of grass and bushes that are regularly marked by other dogs, and to smell out precisely the track taken by pheasant or rabbit when crossing our lane. Once in the fields OM cannot maintain her usual brisk pace while heaving a wheeled vehicle across rough or wet ground, and the calls to me of 'Florrie come *on'* are less frequent.

We were all taken over to the vet recently, apparently for no more serious cause than our annual routine injections. I always used to find a visit to the surgery rather an agreeable social occasion - a needle prick is nothing to the dog of a medical household - but since the extraction of my teeth I have become more cautious. The injections did indeed take place; Daisy made a terrible fuss and the

*... regular teeth cleaning
- a dreadful business*

vet had to shut the surgery door rather hurriedly so her screams should not frighten waiting clients. Our various certificates were completed and once these were stowed in OM's pocket, I prepared to leave.

I was made very apprehensive when OM picked me up, replaced me on the examination table and pointed out a wobbly tooth in my mouth. Before I realised what was happening, that vet had a pair of pliers out and my tooth was in his hand! I made a small squeak but was otherwise very brave. Some uncomplimentary remarks about the quantity of tartar adhering to my remaining teeth were passed, and an alarming suggestion made that I should have this taken off under anaesthetic. Much to my relief, OM rejected this. She accepted instead a tube of dog toothpaste, has bought some baby toothbrushes and Daisy and I now undergo regular teeth-cleaning - a dreadful business, but OM seems to consider it is improving our gums so unfortunately is persisting with the performance.

Very affectionately, Florrie.

Chalk Hill
Spring, my tenth year

Dear Young Mistress,

There is talk of a party to celebrate your homecoming; this has also been mentioned as a final party for this house and I am coming to suspect those extra rooms gradually taking form down on Exmoor are intended for our more permanent occupation.

Really OM and the Master have no idea how to manage building works and the progress is very slow. There is far too much discussion and not nearly enough doing. I could tell them that once the Man I Love had made a decision, action was taken and a wall came down. Admittedly it did take a little longer for it to rise again. We visit most weekends - the pattern is the same: we arrive late afternoon and I generally manage to slip away while the car is being unloaded and make my own survey of progress. The young dogs are less subtle and usually find themselves called back and shut in before they reach the latest patch of wet cement.

OM and the Master have a good look round while it is still daylight, then spend the rest of the evening complaining about what has not been done and what has been done incorrectly. There is one room left furnished downstairs and the heating still functions so we are quite cosy, but it is annoying to be kept out of the new parts, especially as I can detect the builders now take their food breaks indoors. In the morning a number of men arrive and more talking goes on, problems are apparently settled, OM is assured that all will be finished very soon, we take a quick run round the river field and then set off for home.

On the whole I would be in favour of a move to Exmoor. I recall our days at Litton and the adventures we had there with some pride, and I certainly prefer a walk on the moor to the rather tame fields and woods here. Even though making one's way through thick growths of heather is quite strenuous, a small sheep track can usually be found that will avoid such obstacles, and how much more satisfying to put up a curlew or snipe than a fat lazy pheasant.

I think I have made it clear that in very inclement conditions I now prefer to stay by the fire. It would probably not be so convenient for me to accompany the Master to his work places but I have scaled the heights and been proclaimed the President's dog, - perhaps I should be content to retire on this note. Indeed he speaks of retirement himself.

I am looking forward *so much* to hearing the Man I Love call me Bonzo once more.

Ever your most affectionate, Florrie.

I certainly prefer a walk on the moor ...

Tail Piece